A CENTURY OF PROGRESS
SERIES

•

A series of volumes by well-known
scholars presenting the essential
features of those fundamental
sciences which are the foundation
stones of modern industry.

•

A CENTURY OF PROGRESS SERIES

THE UNIVERSE UNFOLDING

The Story of Man's Increasing
Comprehension of the Universe
Around Him

BY

ROBERT H. BAKER, Ph.D.

Professor of Astronomy in the University of Illinois

Author of ASTRONOMY, AN INTRODUCTION

Baltimore

The WILLIAMS & WILKINS COMPANY

AND ASSOCIATES IN COOPERATION WITH

The CENTURY of PROGRESS EXPOSITION

1932

ASSOCIATE PUBLISHERS

THE BAKER AND TAYLOR COMPANY, New York
KROCH'S BOOKSTORE, Chicago.
THE NORMAN, REMINGTON COMPANY, Baltimore.
LIBRARY BOOK HOUSE, Springfield, Mass.
FRANCES MCLEOD BOOKSTALL, Milwaukee.
LEVINSON'S BOOKSTORE, Sacramento.

●

BAILLIÈRE, TINDALL & COX, London.

COMPOSED AND PRINTED AT THE
WAVERLY PRESS, INC.
FOR
THE WILLIAMS & WILKINS COMPANY
BALTIMORE, MD., U S. A.

CONTENTS

LIST OF ILLUSTRATIONS

PREFACE

Our story is about the evolution of the universe. It is not concerned, however, with the origin of the celestial bodies; nor does it deal with the earth's beginning, long before it became the dwelling place of man. It is an account of the universe evolving in the mind of man. The story opens with man already in the scene, looking around him to determine what sort of place the earth may be, and what of the heavens above. We watch the universe unfold before him, at times very slowly, at others with explosive rapidity. The simple scene of yesterday becomes the mighty panorama of today, preparing us for the deeper vistas of tomorrow. It is a story of progress.

The universe of the ancients may be likened to a bud. Encased within the sphere of the stars, whose blue surface seemed to be only a little way beyond the orbit of the planet Saturn, it was a tiny bud indeed. After Copernicus had placed the sun instead of the earth in the center, the starry sphere began to expand. The bud was swelling; but there was as yet no hint of the form of the flower into which it would unfold.

Three centuries ago, the bud burst. The sphere of the stars vanished. And man looked with amazement beyond the place where it had stood to behold throngs of stars arrayed one behind another as far into the distance as the eye could see. During the past century and a half, astronomers have explored the star fields. They have assembled the stars into a great system, the system of the Milky Way, which until very recently comprised the entire known physical universe. Today, we look with new amazement beyond the Milky Way into hitherto unimagined depths of space. We discern millions of external galaxies, millions of light years away.

Our account of the universe unfolding is a story of accomplishment under conditions of the greatest difficulty. Standing on a planet so tiny as to be negligible in comparison with its colossal surroundings, man has devised powerful instruments and methods for exploring the universe. He is arraying the bewildering spectacle of the heavens into a comprehensive scheme. As the scheme unfolds, two things arouse our admiration—the vast universe around us and the mysterious mind of man.

CHAPTER I

THE SPHERE OF THE STARS

NEARLY three thousand years ago, Homer, in the *Iliad*, pictured the universe as it seemed to the early Greeks. The earth's surface is a circular plane surrounded by the ocean. Over it bends the solid, stationary dome of the sky like a protecting mantle, illuminated throughout the day by the sun, and ornamented at night by the stars. Across this dome the sun, moon, and stars pursue their daily courses, rising out of the ocean in the east, and plunging into the ocean again at their setting in the west. But the Great Bear—the Great Dipper—wheels round and round in the northern sky without setting.

The entire universe of these early times was much smaller than the earth. It was simply the limited region of the earth's surface then known, covered by the blue canopy of the sky not very far overhead. The celestial bodies were nearby, and were therefore of small dimensions, small enough in fact to be conveyed easily across the sky. Homer's description of the universe is incidental to the principal story which narrates the siege and destruction of Troy. It is incomplete. In particular, it leaves us in doubt as to how the sun, moon, and stars return to their rising points in the east. Some early peoples imagined that they passed through tunnels; others believed that they were ferried around behind the mountains to the north. The rotating celestial sphere was a more convincing plan.

The sphere of the fixed stars appears first in the sixth century B.C., and is often credited to Anaximenes, one of the Ionian nature philosophers, the most ancient of the Greek Schools. He supposed that the stars are set like diamonds on the inner surface of a sphere, which completely encloses the earth, and which rotates daily from east to west, causing the stars to rise and set. It was a great improvement over the stationary sky, assigning as it did to a single cause the daily motions of all the celestial bodies. For more than two thousand years thereafter, up to and even beyond the time of Copernicus, the sphere of the stars stood almost unquestioned as the boundary of the universe, though the earth at its center soon came to be regarded as a globe rather than a disk.

The universe of the early Greeks is the universe of appearances, as compared with the more fanciful constructions of which we catch glimpses through the mists that envelope more primitive times. It is the universe of today for everyone who can view the earth around him and the sky above with a perfectly open mind. In the meantime, the "fixed" stars have moved a little, and the earth's precessional motion has altered somewhat the directions of the constellations. But appearances, in general, remain the same.

To the observer whose horizon is unobstructed, the earth may well seem to be a circular disk, and the sky a dome resting on the horizon. But when we observe more closely—if, for example, we look out over the ocean, and notice that the superstructure of a ship remains in view after the hull has vanished below the sky line, we conclude that the earth curves downward in the distance. It is now easy to imagine that we are standing on the top of a great globe.

As we watch the stars rising and setting, the sky no longer seems to rest on the earth. We decide, as the ancients did, that it is a complete sphere surrounding the earth which hides its lower half. There is nothing to suggest at once that the stars are not fixed on the surface of the sphere. They seem to be equally distant, and to keep the same relative positions, from day to day and from year to year. And there is nothing to indicate the distance of the sphere of the stars. If it is not very far away, then the stars must be lights of not very great size, twinkling lights of different brightness and color.

As we watch the constellations during an evening, we notice how the sphere of the stars seems to be moving. It is rotating westward, causing the stars to circle around us daily in parallel paths

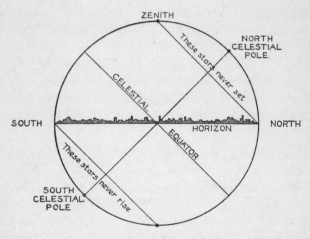

FIG. 1. Daily Rotation of the Sphere of the Stars. For observers in middle northern latitudes.

which are inclined toward the south for observers in middle northern latitudes. A star that rises exactly in the east, or the sun at the equinox, reaches its highest point halfway up in the southern sky, and descends obliquely to its setting exactly in the west. This particular course is along the celestial equator, half of which is above the horizon.

Toward the north, the daily circles come more and more into view, until they are entirely visible. Within a circular region of the northern heavens, the stars wheel around without setting; and the point around which they wheel, the north celestial pole, is closely marked by Polaris, the pole star or north star, at the end of the handle of the Little Dipper. Below the south horizon, an equal circular region centered at the south celestial pole contains the constellations, such as the Southern Cross, which never come into view in middle northern latitudes.

Continuing the examination of the sky from night to night, we soon discover that the rotation of the celestial sphere is completed in slightly less than a day, by the sun. The Pleiades, or "Seven Sisters," for example, rise four minutes earlier from night to night. Each night, therefore, they are a little farther west than they were at the same time the night before. In the early evening in the fall they appear in the eastern sky; in the winter they are high in the south; in spring they are in the west setting soon after the sun. Thus at the same hour throughout the year the constellations march westward with the changing seasons. The explanation of this majestic procession is found in the apparent motion of the sun among the constellations.

The sun moves steadily eastward with respect to the stars, once around in a year, as though it were revolving annually around the earth. Consequently, it lags a little behind the stars in completing the daily circuit westward, causing the march of the constellations which we have just noticed.   Aside from this effect, the sun's eastward movement is not obvious ordinarily, because the stars can not be see in the daytime.   In the planetarium, where the celestial motions are faithfully represented, except that they are accelerated for convenience, the light of the sun is dimmed so that it does not hide the stars.   Here we can observe the sun's motion very clearly.   Its annual course, the ecliptic, is a great circle inclined $23\frac{1}{2}°$ to the celestial equator.

Seven bright celestial bodies move against the background of the constellations.   They are the sun, moon, and five bright planets.   All move eastward, in paths which are nearly circular and only slightly inclined to the sun's path, so that they never wander very far from the ecliptic.   The moon makes the circuit of the heavens in $27\frac{1}{3}$ days. The planets have periods ranging from 88 days for Mercury to nearly thirty years for Saturn.   Although they make progress toward the east, the planets halt at intervals and countermarch for a time, westward. They pursue looped paths which are demonstrated in a convincing way by the faster motions of the planetarium.

These features of the heavens which we observe today were well known to the early Greeks, and were the basis of their idea of the universe. In Plato's dialogues we read that the universe is bounded by the sphere of the fixed stars, which turns daily from east to west around an axis through the earth. The earth at the center is a stationary globe. The eastward motions of the planets, like those of the sun and moon, are inclined to the direction of the daily motion. The seven celestial bodies which revolve around the earth, between it and the sphere of the stars, in order of distance from the earth are: the moon, Mercury and Venus, the sun, Mars, Jupiter, and Saturn. This arrangement is in the order of decreasing swiftness of their movements relative to the stars. The stars themselves were supposed to be not far beyond Saturn.

The study of the stars could not make appreciable progress until the invention of the telescope, the spectroscope, the photographic plate, and other products of modern ingenuity. For by far the greater part of the time that man has watched the moving spectacle displayed on the deep blue screen of the evening skies, the stars have been for him simply twinkling points of light differing one from another only in brightness, color, and direction, that is to say, position on the celestial sphere. They served, of course, as they still serve, as useful points of reference for telling the time of night, for anticipating the changing of the seasons, as guides to the traveler on land and sea, and as landmarks for the study of the planetary movements.

To the ancient astronomer the stars presented no problem comparable in interest with that of the seven wanderers. The stars set the stage. But the planets, and the sun and moon seemed to deserve special consideration. They were the actors in the celestial drama, whose movements must be followed attentively. And these astronomers were quite correct, as we shall see. The stars could not assume their rightful significance in the picture until the relations of the planetary bodies were more clearly understood.

It was evident enough to the early astronomers that the rising and setting of the celestial bodies could be accounted for equally well if the earth is moving. But this alternative was so inconsistent with the common sense of the times that only a few ventured to give it serious consideration. Heracleides of Pontus, in the fourth century B.C., was perhaps the first to believe that the daily motion of the heavens from east to west is caused simply by the rotation of the earth in the opposite direction.

Aristarchus of Samos, in the third century B.C., went still further. He held not only that the earth rotates, but also that it revolves annually around the sun, and that the stars, inasmuch as they seem not to shift back and forth as we revolve, must be very remote indeed. But there was no convincing evidence available at the time to support this theory. For nearly two thousand years more, the earth lay motionless in the minds of its inhabitants. And during this long interval, the revolutions of the planets around the stationary earth were explained almost entirely by the theory of epicycles.

This plan was proposed by the mathematician Apollonius of Perga, who lived in the third century B.C. also. In the simplest case, the motion of a planet was regarded as the resultant of two uniform, circular motions. The planet itself moves around a smaller circle, the epicycle, whose center is describing a larger circle around the earth. In this way the planet could proceed in a succession of loops, as it is observed to do; and the motion could be made still more irregular by placing the earth out of the center of the larger circle. Fortunate combinations of these and other geometrical devices might well represent the complex motions of the sun, moon, and planets. So it seemed to Apollonius, although he did not work out the details.

The theory of epicycles was soon elevated to the foremost place in astronomical practice, where it remained for nearly two thousand years. Hipparchus, in the second century B.C., generally regarded as the greatest of ancient astronomers, adopted the plan and applied it especially to the movements of the sun and moon. Ptolemy, in the second century A.D., extended the theory to explain the looped motions of the planets. For this reason, and because we find an account of the procedure in his great work, the *Almagest*, the theory of epicycles is known as the Ptolemaic theory.

In 1543, the Polish astronomer Copernicus set forth his theory of the moving earth, that it rotates daily from west to east, and revolves annually around the sun in the same direction. The planets still moved in epicycles, thirty-four in all, to produce the observed irregularities. But the largest epicycles of the geocentric theory, which were designed to account for the looped motions of the planets, had now disappeared. The new construction was simpler than the old, and at the same time was equally effective. Proof of the moving

earth was not yet available, but able champions
came forward to uphold the new theory.

In the Copernican system the earth took its
rightful place as one of the planets revolving

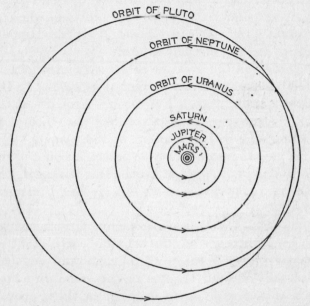

FIG. 2. Orbits of the Principal Planets. The orbits of Mercury,
Venus, and the earth are within the orbit of Mars. Actually the
orbits are not exactly circular, nor in the same plane.

around the sun. The membership of the planetary system, in order of distance from the sun,
was now: Mercury, Venus, the earth accompanied

by its satellite, the moon, Mars, Jupiter, and
Saturn (Plate 1). Beyond Saturn was the sphere
of the fixed stars, intact for a little while longer,
but now as motionless as were the stars themselves
upon it, apparently turning daily from east to west
because of the earth's rotation from west to east.

The sphere of the stars had been placed by
Ptolemy only a little way beyond the orbit of
Saturn. Relieved now of its responsibility of
rotating daily around the earth, this sphere could
be larger. Indeed, it had to be larger. Otherwise, as Copernicus pointed out, the constellations would seem to shift back and forth annually
as we circle around the sun.

There was as yet no reason, however, for assigning to the sphere of the stars anything like the
dimensions of the present universe. If this
sphere were only seven hundred times more remote
than our distance from the sun, the extreme shift
of the stars would not exceed ten minutes of arc, or
one third of the moon's apparent diameter. A
displacement of this size of all the stars in the
same region of the sky could not have been noticed
with the instruments of that time. It was not
the modern problem of the relative parallax of a
nearby star against the background of more remote
stars; for the stars were still believed to be equally
far away.

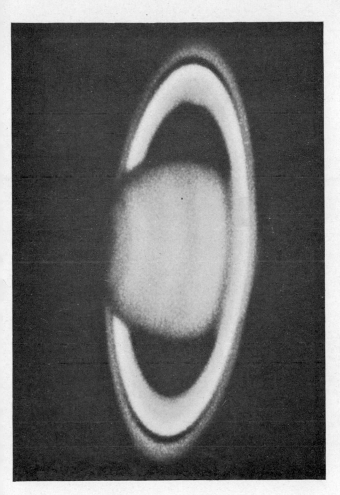

PLATE 1. Saturn and its Rings. The most distant planet known to the ancients. (Photographed by Barnard. By courtesy of Yerkes Observatory.)

The universe of Copernicus was not necessarily enormous. With the sun in the center, the celestial sphere might have been only eighteen times farther removed than the recently discovered planet Pluto, and therefore scarcely more than a quarter of one per cent of the actual distance of the nearest star. It was still a universe in a nutshell—the spherical shell on which the stars were set.

The new heliocentric universe was, nevertheless, capable of indefinite expansion. Already, the sphere of the stars was much larger than the earlier astronomers had imagined it. It was soon to swell further, and then to burst; and out of it the universe was to unfold in the minds of those who came after Copernicus, at times with surprising rapidity, into the colossal structure we behold today, a structure still unfolding.

CHAPTER II

THE BURSTING OF THE BARRIERS

THE heliocentric theory of Copernicus gave greater freedom to the imaginations of those who observed and reflected about the heavens. With the earth and the other planets now subservient to the sun, the stars began to be regarded in a new light; they might well be suns themselves, perhaps also attended by planetary systems. Accordingly, the sun is a star. Soon after its promotion by Copernicus to the dominating position in the universe, it was reduced to a station of merely local importance, as one of the multitude of stars, brighter for us because of its proximity. Before the close of the sixteenth century, Giordano Bruno believed that the stars are distant suns, so remote in fact that it would be difficult for a very long time to decide whether they are fixed or in motion. And the sun in its new rôle as a star might be moving also.

Long-established traditions concerning the heavens were being discarded along with the acceptance of the earth's revolution, among them the conception of the objective existence of the celestial sphere. For two thousand years, this sphere

14

of the fixed stars had set the boundary of the physical universe; it had stood unquestioned as the impassible limit of space, beyond which was mystery. Probably no distinguished scientist after Copernicus believed in the reality of this sphere of the ancients. It might still, it is true, be a sphere *full of stars*; it certainly could not be a spherical surface *set with stars*. Although definite proof was not yet available, it was generally understood that the stars are not all at the same distance.

With the bursting of the celestial barriers the stars, removed from their settings on the curved interior of the sky, came now to be regarded as distributed indefinitely through space. But a universe of stars extending monotonously to infinity offered scarcely more encouragement to the investigator than a universe enclosed in a shell. For two centuries after the time of Copernicus, the attention of astronomers was centered in the remarkable developments within the solar system. Observations of the stars were intended chiefly to determine their directions more precisely, so that they could serve faithfully as landmarks for charting the positions and motions of the planetary bodies.

Nevertheless, some progress was made during this interval in observing the stars on their own account.   Tycho Brahe was astonished by the outburst of a star, in 1572, in the constellation Cassiopeia, which rapidly attained a brightness equal to that of Venus, and in the following six months faded gradually from view. Kepler, in 1604, observed a "new star" in Ophiuchus, which at the height of its temporary splendor rivaled Jupiter in brightness.   Galileo, in 1610, with the recently invented telescope saw a multitude of stars where the unaided eye could discern only a few, and observed for the first time that the Milky Way is an assemblage of stars.

Beginning in 1650 with Mizar, in the handle of the Great Dipper, a few stars were casually recorded as being resolved by the telescope into pairs of stars; and a few of the brighter nebulae and star clusters were noticed.   Halley, in 1718, was the first to demonstrate that the stars are moving.   These pioneer observations gave hints of the revelations in store for the astronomer, when he should finally turn his attention from the solar system to explore the great star fields beyond.

The first picture of the organization of the stars in a vast finite system was sketched, in 1750, by Thomas Wright of Durham, England, in his book entitled *An Original Theory of the Universe.* Wright's "grindstone theory" is based on the appearance of the Milky Way.   This luminous girdle around the heavens, which the telescope resolves into myriads of stars, suggests that the system of stars to which the sun belongs has roughly the form of a circular disk whose thickness is small in comparison with the diameter. Through the disk the stars are scattered promiscuously. The sun has a nearly central position. In all directions from the earth along the principal plane of the disk the greatest numbers of stars are projected on the sky, and their combined light produces the Milky Way.

It remained for Immanuel Kant, who adopted and clarified Wright's theory of the construction of the stellar system, to erect upon it a still more colossal and comprehensive speculative structure. In his *Theorie des Himmels*, which bears the date 1755, but which was distributed several years later, Kant proposes a succession of celestial systems of increasing order. Beginning with the solar system, the next step in the series is the system of the Milky Way, the galactic system, an assemblage of many suns, and perhaps of planetary bodies attending them. The system of next higher order comprises many galaxies, ours and others like it; it is the unit again in a system of still higher order. Kant regarded the nebulae as exterior stellar systems, beyond our Milky Way, themselves milky ways. To this "island universe theory," long favored, afterwards rejected, and now revived and flourishing in a slightly different form, we shall return later.

J. H. Lambert, Alsatian contemporary of Wright and Kant, held somewhat similar views concerning the structure of the galactic system and the hierarchy of systems—systems upon systems, continuing to the limit of the imagination. "Thus everything revolves—the earth round the sun; the sun round the center of his system; this system round a center common to it with other systems; this group, this assemblage of systems, round a center which is common to it with other groups of the same kind; and where shall we have done?"

Speculation was now far in advance of observational support, so far, in fact, that it would ordinarily be regarded as having little significance. But these three daring individuals have proved in many respects to be true prophets, especially in the light of recent discoveries. Scrutinizing the opening bud of the universe they perceived a colorful, complex flower, while their predecessors and many who followed them could envisage only a drab, indefinitely extended structure, any part of which was a fair sample of the remainder. Wright, Kant, and Lambert blazed the trail to the Milky Way and into the depths beyond for the explorer to follow with his "line and plummet." They share with him the honors due to successful pioneers.

William Herschel, in England, was the first astronomer to make extensive systematic explorations beyond the solar system. He is known therefore as the founder of sidereal astronomy. Over his grave are inscribed the words: *coelorum perrupit claustra*—"he broke through the barriers of the heavens." He was indeed the first to explore the stellar system as a structure of three dimensions. Musician of distinction, builder of great reflecting telescopes, discoverer of the planet Uranus and other features of the solar system, Herschel's self-imposed scientific mission in life was to inquire into the construction of the heavens; with this objective he began, in 1775, his review of the heavens. In contrast with the many centuries in which astronomy has been pursued, the problem of the structure of the universe as a scientific problem is no older than the United States of America.

To an observer in the midst of a wood the shortest way out might be the direction in which the trees appear to be least numerous. It is more nearly true, if the trees are distributed with some sort of uniformity, and if the wood is small enough so that the trees at the edge can be seen. An analogous situation is presented to the observer

within the galactic system. In order to simplify
his problem, Herschel assumed at first, as Wright
did, that the stars are distributed more or less
uniformly, and that his telescope could penetrate
to the boundaries of the system. Other things
being equal, the distance to the border in any
direction is then proportional to the cube root of
the number of stars in a given area of the sky in
that direction. If, for example, the numbers of
stars counted in two directions are respectively
64 and 27, the corresponding distances to the
edge of the system are as four is to three.

Herschel's procedure was to make "gauges," or
counts, of the stars visible in the field of his 19-inch
reflecting telescope when it was directed successively to different parts of the heavens. The
field of view was 15′ in diameter, or about one
fourth the apparent area of the full moon. In
some regions only two or three stars could be seen,
while in the richest part of the Milky Way the
count ran as high as 588 stars. In all, he made
3400 gauges from which the relative distances to
the visible boundaries of the stellar system could be
calculated according to the rule, and thus the form
of the system, as far as it could be seen. The
form was that of a rough grindstone, as Wright
had conjectured, having a diameter five or six
times its thickness, but a cloven grindstone—split

around a third of its circumference corresponding to the great dark rift which divides the Milky Way into parallel streams over this fraction of its circular course.

The "cloven grindstone theory" too was simple, as pioneer theories are likely to be; and, as Herschel himself soon recognized and announced, the underlying assumptions are fallacious. The distribution of the stars is far from uniform. The stars are gathered into clusters and great clouds, and regions teeming with stars are abruptly interrupted by dark areas in which few stars can be discerned.

But especially fatal to the fortunate outcome of Herschel's gauges was the small distance which his telescope could penetrate into the depths of space— only as far as the stars of the fifteenth magnitude. In no direction could he look through to the edge of the system. His "universe," some six thousand light years in diameter, was simply that portion of the vast galactic system in the sun's vicinity which lay within his view. Necessarily roughly symmetrical with respect to the sun, it gave little indication of the character of the system as a whole, except by its greater extension in the plane of the Milky Way.

Such was the result of the first systematic attack on the problem of the construction of the

heavens. It exhibited, at least, some of the diffi-
culties which subsequent explorers would have to
overcome, and gave warning that a satisfactory
solution of the great problem would require a long
time. Herschel's gauges were only a small part of
his investigations into the construction of the
heavens. His extensive surveys with large telescopes of his own making revealed a variety of
sidereal phenomena hitherto unnoticed. He observed and catalogued multitudes of double stars,
some of them certainly in mutual revolution,
clusters of stars, and nebulae of different kinds.
With his discoveries astronomy became in fact the
science of the stars.

John Herschel, who extended his father's gauges
to the southern sky, observing at the Cape of
Good Hope, came to regard the Milky Way as a
thin flat ring of stars surrounding the scattered
stars within, rather than the projection of a disk of
stars. It was easier to picture its dark lanes as
openings in a ring, instead of trying to imagine
them as long radial tunnels. This construction
could have been avoided if he had known, as we
now know, that the lanes in the Milky Way are
caused by the intervention of celestial dust clouds.

Gradually thereafter a more valuable idea
gained ground, expressed clearly by Proctor in
England as early as 1869, namely, that ,the Milky

27-020

3

Way consists of clouds of stars arranged in streams in space *at different distances*. Easton, of Rotterdam, went further; he presented evidence intended to show that this concourse of star clouds has the form of a double-armed spiral, resembling the spectacular spiral nebulae. Here we have a reminder of Kant's "island universe" theory which had been in disfavor for half a century, and was not to be definitely revived for a quarter of a century more.

J. C. Kapteyn, at Groningen in Holland, inaugurated the modern statistical study of the construction of the galactic system. In 1906, he proposed the plan of selected areas—about two hundred rather small areas uniformly distributed over the sky from pole to pole, and altogether as representative as possible of the sky as a whole—to which he invited the concerted attention of astronomers. Investigations of the numbers, brightness, motions, distances, and special characteristics of the stars in these areas were to provide the data for a new attempt to solve the great problem.

Kapteyn's last report of progress, shortly before his death in 1922, showed how the stars thin out with increasing distance from the sun, least rapidly in the direction of the Milky Way, most rapidly at right angles to it, until at the distance of 27,000 light years in the former direction and 5400 light years in the latter the star-density is reduced to a hundredth of its value near the sun. These great distances are expressed in light years rather than in miles in order to avoid inconveniently large numbers. The light year, the distance light travels in a year, is about six million million miles.

Modern counts of stars differ from Herschel's gauges in two important respects. The stars are counted on photographs of the different areas of the sky. Photographs with the 100-inch telescope on Mount Wilson show thirty times as many stars as Herschel could see. But the chief difficulty in the present investigations is not the great numbers of stars to be counted; it is in knowing what stars to include. For the counts are now made by classes with respect to brightness, that is to say, by *magnitudes*.

A star of the first magnitude is a bright star; it is $2\frac{1}{2}$ times brighter than a star of the second magnitude, which in turn is $2\frac{1}{2}$ times brighter than a third magnitude star. This numerical rule can be extended so as to denote the magnitude of any object whose brightness has been measured. A star of the sixth magnitude is barely visible to the naked eye. Higher numbers are for stars which can be seen only with the aid of the telescope. With the 100-inch telescope it is possible to photograph a star as faint as the twenty-first magnitude, which is a hundred million times ($2\frac{1}{2}$ raised to the twentieth power) fainter than one of the first magnitude. There are a few stars brighter than the first magnitude, which according to the rule must be given smaller numbers. The magnitude of Sirius, the brightest of all the stars, is -1.6.

Evidently, the magnitude of a star as we see it depends on its actual brightness and its distance from us. If all the stars were of the same intrinsic brightness and at the same distance, they would have the same magnitude. If they were of the same intrinsic brightness and at different distances, they would appear of different brightness, and their magnitudes would inform us of their relative distances. Consider two of these stars, of the first and the second magnitude. The latter, being $2\frac{1}{2}$ times fainter than the former, must be 1.6 times more remote, since the brightness of a star varies inversely as the square of its distance. Accordingly, stars of magnitudes 2, 3, 4, 5, 6 . . . . . are respectively 1.6, 2.5, 4.0, 6.4, 10.0 . . . . . times more remote than those of the first magnitude. In counting stars in an area by magnitudes the astronomer is counting the numbers that lie at different distances from the earth.

With the assumption of equal intrinsic brightness, all stars of the same magnitude lie on the surface of a sphere whose center is the earth. All stars exactly one magnitude fainter lie on the surface of a sphere whose radius is 1.6 times the radius of the first sphere, and whose volume is therefore nearly four times the greater. Accordingly, if the stars are uniformly distributed through space, the total number must become four times greater for each fainter magnitude that is counted. If the increase in any direction is faster or slower, the stars are becoming more congested or are thinning out as we proceed in that direction. Thus by counting stars of successive magnitudes, it is possible to determine their general arrangement in the space around us, as far as the telescope can penetrate.

This is the basis of the present statistical approach to the construction of the galactic system. It must be understood that the stars are not all of the same actual brightness; but variety in this respect does not invalidate the conclusions when many stars are concerned. The difficulty in obtaining the data from the photographs is not in the counting, as we have said before, but in knowing what stars to count. The magnitudes must be determined, and this requires a very great amount of work when tens of thousands of stars are involved.

The total numbers of stars in the whole sky brighter than successive photographic magnitudes, totals which are readily calculated from the counts in the selected areas, are shown in Table 1. It is interesting to notice that the ratio of increase for each added magnitude is nowhere as much as four, the factor that would be expected, as we have seen, if the stars were uniformly distributed.

TABLE 1

Total Number of Stars Brighter than a Specified Photographic Magnitude

MAGNITUDE LIMIT	TOTAL NUMBER	MAGNITUDE LIMIT	TOTAL NUMBER
4.0	360	13.0	2,720,000
5.0	1,030	14.0	6,500,000
6.0	2,940	15.0	15,000,000
7.0	8,200	16.0	33,000,000
8.0	22,800	17.0	70,000,000
9.0	62,000	18.0	143,000,000
10.0	166,000	19.0	275,000,000
11.0	431,000	20.0	505,000,000
12.0	1,100,000	21.0	890,000,000

Thus the stars thin out, in general, with increasing distance from the earth, and faster at greater distances as shown by the fainter magnitudes. But even for the faintest stars photographed with the 100-inch telescope at Mount Wilson the total number is nearly doubled when the limit is extended a single magnitude further. At the great distance of the average star of the twenty-first magnitude we are still far from the outer edge of the stellar system. The impressive total of nearly a thousand million stars within reach of this telescope is only three per cent of the number in the whole galactic system, according to Seares' estimate.

When the counts of stars in the selected areas are arranged with respect to distance from the Milky Way, it appears, as we have already noticed, that the stars thin out with increasing distance from the earth least rapidly in the direction of the Milky Way; and the rate of thinning increases symmetrically above and below this circle of star clouds. The first rough picture of the portion of the stellar system within the reach of the 100-inch telescope shows it "in the form of a much flattened swarm of bees with the densest part of the swarm in the center." This is the "Kapteyn universe," a larger edition of Herschel's "grindstone."

In this first approximation the sun is nearly central. Unquestionably it is near the central plane; but thus far the counts were pooled for all the areas around the sky on circles parallel to the Milky Way, so that there was as yet no certainty of the sun's central position in the stellar system. Indeed, as we look along the course of the Milky Way, we are impressed by its great brilliancy in

the region of the constellation Sagittarius, and its
much feebler aspect in the opposite direction,
toward Auriga. If there is a degree of symmetry
in the galactic system, we must be nearer its
boundary in the latter direction. This was the
next step in the statistical program, to establish
the eccentric location of the sun. Here a compli-
cation enters.

When the counts are arranged with reference to
the location of the selected areas around the course
of the Milky Way, Seares finds that the region in
which the stars are most numerous—supposedly in
the direction of the center of the system—depends
on the limiting brightness of the stars included in
the counts. For the bright stars it is in the direction of the constellation Carina. As successively
fainter stars are added to the counts the direction
in which the stars are most numerous moves eastward along the Milky Way, until for the faintest
stars it becomes fairly stationary in the region of
the constellation Sagittarius. A double distribution of the stars around us is indicated—a local
star cloud which dominates the foreground of the
sidereal scenery, and the general Milky Way
system, to which the fainter, more distant stars
chiefly belong.

Nearly a century ago, John Herschel drew
attention to a zone of bright stars which cuts

across the Milky Way at a considerable angle, and "whose appearance would lead us to suspect that our nearest neighbors in the sidereal system form part of a subordinate sheet or stratum . . ." The American astronomer Gould, in 1874, pointed out that this rather narrow zone of bright stars extends completely around the heavens, forming a great circle as well defined as the Milky Way itself. Inclined 12° to the Milky Way and crossing it in the region of the constellation Cassiopeia in the north and of the Southern Cross in the south, this belt includes the brightest stars in Orion, Taurus, Cassiopeia, Cygnus, Lyra, Scorpius, and around through the southern sky to Canis Major.

From the star-counts the "local system," to which the zone of bright stars belongs, appears as a much flattened, slightly tilted cloud of stars having its center not far from the sun in the direction of Carina. The stars which are visible to the naked eye and with telescopes of moderate size belong mostly to this cloud. More powerful telescopes can penetrate beyond the local system to the fields of stars which follow the arrangement of the galactic system itself. The center of this greater system is far removed from the sun in the direction of the star clouds of Sagittarius. These conclusions, set forth by Seares in 1927, characterize the second stage of the statistical program.

In the meantime, other researches were converging on the great problem of the construction of the heavens. Two of them are especially significant in the present connection. Shapley, at the Mount Wilson Observatory, had succeeded in measuring the distances of the globular star clusters. He showed, in 1918, that these remarkable assemblages of stars constitute a vast system symmetrical with the Milky Way, some 200,000 light years in diameter, whose center is 50,000 light years from the sun in the direction of a point in Sagittarius, almost exactly the same as the direction of the center of the galactic system established later by the star-counts.

Equally significant was Shapley's demonstration, in 1923, that the system N.G.C. 6822 is more remote than the structure outlined by the globular clusters. Hubble, in 1925, presented convincing evidence to show that the bright spiral in Triangulum (Plate 2) is an external system also. It was soon evident that all the spiral nebulae and many other assemblages of stars lie far beyond the confines of our galactic system—that they are themselves great galaxies.

Thus at the close of the first quarter of the present century, the universe was unfolding with spectacular rapidity. Parts of the picture were coming into view very clearly, parts only, but enough to arouse great interest and anticipation, not only among scientists, but among the general public as well. It was now possible to fill in tentatively some of the missing parts of the picture, and thus to sketch the general plan of the visible universe more comprehensively than before—a working sketch subject to alteration and elaboration by future researches. The main features of the sketch which, as recently as 1928, received the approval of many astronomers, were as follows:

Our galactic system is a flattened aggregation of many tens of thousands of millions of stars. Approximately circular in outline, its diameter is 200,000 light years, and its thickness is about one tenth as great. From opposite sides of the central nucleus, some 30,000 light years across, two great streams of star clouds emerge, and coil around in the same sense and in the same plane, like the arms of one of the distant spiral nebulae. Our galactic system is, in fact, a spiral nebula, according to this view, resembling the spiral in Triangulum (Plate 2), though larger,—one of the multitude of spirals, just as our sun is one of many stars.

About halfway from the center toward the edge, in the direction of the constellation Auriga, the sun is located near the center of the local system, a flat star cloud or group of clouds as much as 10,000 light years across, tilted 12° to the principal plane of the greater system.   The other star clouds seen in projection form the circular band of the Milky Way whose brightest part, in Sagittarius (Plate 4), marks the direction of the center 50,000 light years distant from the sun.   Dust clouds enter in an important way in the constitution of the great system, and obscure parts of it from our view. Separated from the galactic system by distances which must be reckoned in millions of light years are other spirals, and assemblages of different form as well—the external galaxies.

The sketch of our galactic system is admittedly rough—a few pencil marks to block in the principal features, so far as they have been noticed, and estimates of a few distances to give some idea of the scale.   The filling in of even the more significant details will require the concerted efforts of astronomers for many years.   It is not an easy matter for observers within this system to represent its different parts in their true relations.   We can not see the woods clearly because of the trees. A bird's eye view of our system from one of the nearer external galaxies would be more immediately instructive.   Moreover, our first sketch shows only a stationary system.   The finished picture must be dynamic—a moving picture.

In the first two chapters we have reviewed some of the principal steps in the advancement of our knowledge of the heavens during the past three thousand years. These great advances have been brought about by the persistent devotion of many astronomers, a devotion stimulated by the driving desire of man to know about the things around him and his relation to this scheme of things. We have watched the swelling and bursting of the tiny spherical bud of ancient times, and its gradual unfolding.

After the age of Copernicus, astronomers began to look through the sphere of the fixed stars to the seemingly illimitable star fields beyond. With the aid of the telescope they gazed with astonishment at millions of stars which had now become correctly in their minds millions of suns. At length, the maze of stars assumed the status of an orderly system whose precise form remained to be learned, and whose membership greatly increased as it was more fully comprehended, from millions to tens of thousands of millions of stars. The boundaries of the galactic system became the new barriers of the heavens; within them was the visible universe; beyond them was the unknown. Wright and Kant had written of universes external to ours, but this speculation had fallen into disfavor in the absence of observational evidence to support it.

Only a few years ago, the second array of barriers burst, and man looked at the heavens with new astonishment to view millions of vast stellar systems extending into the distance as far as the greatest telescope can penetrate. These external galaxies cluster as the stars do. Whether in further analogy they are assembled in a single system, the metagalaxy, whose boundaries will form a third array of barriers we can for the present only imagine.

In historical order the statistical method of investigating the construction of the heavens comes first. Until very recent times it was the only available approach to the problem. Accordingly, we have described first of all this process and its results, from William Herschel to the present time. The usefulness of the statistical method is limited, as those who have employed it have recognized. Viewing the celestial scenery in the average, it smoothes out many of the interesting and significant irregularities, the star clusters and star clouds, and the obstructing dust clouds. It seeks to portray with sweeping strokes of a coarse brush the intricate structure we wish to comprehend, and it does not show clearly the scale of the picture. Provisionally we have filled in missing details by analogy with the spiral nebulae, and we have drawn on the results of the newer photometric method for the dimensions.

Knowledge of the distances of the celestial

bodies is of great value in astronomical inquiries of almost any kind. It is of the first importance in the problem of the structure of the universe. If we knew the distance as well as the direction of every object in the galactic system, it would be possible in theory to construct a faithful model of the system, and thus to solve the problem completely. To make such a model would, of course, take practically forever.

As a substitute for this enormous undertaking, let us suppose that we know or are able to determine the distances of many celestial objects of a particular type, whose distribution through the system conforms to that of the stars in general. The model which exhibits the arrangement of the special objects is the required model of the whole system. This is the plan of the newer and probably much more effective photometric method of investigating the structure of the universe. We turn, therefore, to the important subject of celestial distances and their measurement.

CHAPTER III

THE DISTANCES OF THE STARS

AT THE beginning of the "century of progress" whose achievements are commemorated by the Chicago World's Fair of 1933, astronomers had been unable to measure the distance of a single object beyond the solar system. As late as the opening of the twentieth century, the distances of scarcely sixty stars had become known, and the majority of these were not very accurately known. Today, the distances of more than two thousand stars have been determined by the original direct method, while those of thousands more are rapidly being calculated through the use of recently discovered methods. And with this increase in the number of trustworthy distances the power of astronomical inquiry has increased enormously.

The oldest and most direct way of measuring the distance of a star is by observing its parallax, that is to say, the change in its direction when the star is viewed from two different places. The parallax method is as ancient as man himself. We view the world with our two eyes from two different directions. From the two points of observation we are able to estimate the relative distances of objects fairly close at hand. The character of the parallax effect is more clearly shown when one eye is employed at a time.

If a nearby object is observed with the two eyes alternately, it seems to shift back and forth against a more distant background. For a second object a little farther away, the shift is smaller; and for a third still farther away, say at the distance of two hundred feet, the effect can scarcely be noticed. Experience shows, therefore, that the parallax of an object diminishes as its distance increases, for a particular separation of the two points of observation. By increasing the separation, the distance of the object remaining the same, the parallax is made larger—if, for example, we substitute for the two eyes two observers some distance apart.

The greatest possible separation on the earth is obtained by stationing two observers at diametrically opposite points on the equator. From two such stations the difference in the moon's directions is nearly two degrees, or four times its apparent diameter. The corresponding difference for the sun is only $17''.6$, showing that the sun is about four hundred times more remote than the moon; curiously enough, it is also four hundred times the larger, so that the sun and moon appear to us as disks of very nearly the same size. The nearest star is 275,000 times more remote than the sun. The difference between its directions for our two observers is 0″.00006, about the size of one of the periods on this page viewed at the distance of five hundred miles. No telescope can show a parallax as small as this.

Greater separation of the observers would be accomplished by sending one of them to another

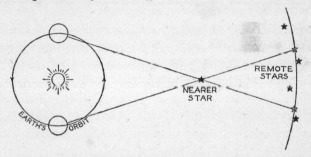

FIG. 3. The Parallax of a Star.   As the earth revolves around the sun, the neighboring star seems to shift back and forth with respect to the more remote stars.

planet. But there is a better plan. Let us observe the difference between the directions of a star at intervals of six months, when the earth is at opposite points of its great orbit around the sun. While the earth's diameter is less than eight thousand miles, the long diameter of its orbit is nearly 186 million miles. Our first enthusiasm for the new procedure is somewhat dampened by a little calculation which shows that the difference in direction for even the nearest star is not greater than the size of a period on this page viewed at the distance of a hundred feet. And this is the most favorable case. It is evident that the measurement of a star's distance by observing its parallax is a serious undertaking, requiring large telescopes, refined methods, and skillful observers.

For a long time, the principal incentive in the many attempts to observe the parallaxes of the stars was to prove conclusively the Copernican doctrine of the earth's revolution around the sun. The desired proof, however, came forth from a hitherto unsuspected quarter when Bradley at the Greenwich Observatory, in 1727, discovered the annually periodic shifting of the stars' positions produced by the aberration of their light. Thereafter, the attempts to measure the parallaxes of the stars were made solely in the interests of the distances. But for more than a century to come, the attempts were destined to be unsuccessful.

Finally, in 1838, Bessel at Königsberg announced that he had observed the parallax of the double star 61 Cygni. The exceptionally rapid motion of this star, straight ahead relative to its neighbors in the sky, had stamped it as probably nearer than the others, and therefore as a promising subject for this particular inquiry. In addition, he found it shifting back and forth annually through an angle of $0''.6$, the parallax effect for a star at the distance two thirds of a million times the earth's distance from the sun. Parallaxes of other stars became known, but the list lengthened very slowly until the photographic plate replaced the eye at the telescope.

In the course of his photographic studies with the 40-inch telescope of the Yerkes Observatory, Schlesinger, in 1903, developed methods of observation and reduction which greatly increased the accuracy of direct parallax determinations. The modern period of these investigations, which he inaugurated, is characterised by concerted activity with large telescopes at a dozen observatories in different parts of the world. As a consequence of this campaign the direct parallaxes of more than two thousand stars are already known.

Photographs of the region of the sky which includes the star under investigation are taken at opposite seasons of the year. The changes in the position of this star with respect to comparison stars—stars which appear near it, but which are presumably so much farther away that they do not appreciably exhibit the parallax displacement—are carefully measured on the plates. Usually the observations must extend over several years in order to separate the periodic parallax effect from the star's own proper motion in a straight line. When the full range of the parallax oscillation has been determined, it is the custom to regard one-half of it as the star's parallax; it is the heliocentric parallax, that is to say, the greatest difference between the directions of the star as viewed from the earth and the sun.

When the parallax of a celestial body has been measured, it is a simple matter to calculate the distance; and there is a choice of units in which to express it. Interstellar distances are so vast that their expression in miles involves inconveniently large numbers. Sirius, for example, the brightest star and one of the nearest, is distant about 50 million million miles. It is more than half a million times the earth's distance from the sun, which is the astronomical unit frequently employed for measurements in the solar system. For the stars astronomers prefer a still larger unit of distance, either the parsec or the light year.

"Parsec" is the abbreviated way of saying "the distance at which a star would have a parallax of one second of arc." The length of this great yardstick is 19.2 million million miles. The distance in parsecs is the reciprocal of the parallax in seconds of arc. Since the parallax of Sirius is 0″.37, its distance is 2.7 parsecs.

The light year is the distance traversed by light

in one year, at the rate of nearly 186,300 miles a second—nearly six million million miles. Three and a quarter light years equal one parsec. Thus the distance of Sirius is 8.8 light years. Evidently, either one of these large units is convenient for expressing the distances of the nearer stars. For the external galaxies, however, where the numbers again run into millions, still larger units, the kiloparsec and megaparsec, are sometimes employed.

A dozen stars, counting a double star as one, are now known to be nearer than 61 Cygni. Including this star, we have, in Table 2, a list of thirteen stars whose distances are less than eleven light years.

In advance we might have supposed that this list of the sun's nearest neighbors would contain only the most brilliant stars in the sky. It does include, it is true, the brightest star of all, Sirius, and two others, Alpha Centauri and Procyon, which rank among the brightest. Yet seven of the thirteen are invisible to the naked eye; their magnitudes are numbered larger than six. Evidently the stars vary enormously in actual brightness. This conclusion is important. The apparent brightness of a star tells us very little about its distance; a faint star that is visible only with a large telescope may be close at hand and intrinsically faint, or it may be very remote and actually very bright. On the average, however, when many stars are considered together, the brightest stars must be the nearest.

Nearest of all is a telescopic star of the tenth magnitude, which is known appropriately as

TABLE 2

STARS NEARER THAN ELEVEN LIGHT YEARS

| NAME | MAGNI-TUDE | PARALLAX | DISTANCE | |
			Parsecs	Light years
Proxima Centauri.	10.5	0″.783	1.28	4.16
Alpha Centauri.	0.1	.757	1.32	4.30
Barnard's star.	9.7	.538	1.86	6.06
Wolf 359.	13	.404	2.48	8.08
Lalande 21185.	7.6	.392	2.55	8.31
Sirius.	−1.6	.371	2.70	8.80
B. D.—12° 4523.	10	.350	2.86	9.32
Innes' star.	12	.340	2.94	9.58
Kapteyn's star.	9.2	.317	3.16	10.3
Tau Ceti.	3.6	.315	3.17	10.3
Procyon.	0.5	.312	3.21	10.4
Epsilon Eridani.	3.8	.310	3.23	10.5
61 Cygni.	5.0	.300	3.33	10.9

"Proxima." It was assigned this place of distinction in 1915, through the observations of Innes at the Union Observatory in South Africa. Proxima never rises above the horizon in the latitude of Chicago. In southern skies it is located scarcely more than two degrees from the bright double star Alpha Centauri, long supposed to be the nearest, with which it is closely associated. The three stars are moving together through the stellar system.

As the earth revolves around the sun, therefore, the nearer stars seem to describe tiny parallax orbits annually, and the size of the apparent orbit informs us of the star's distance. For more distant stars the annual displacements are smaller, and the distance determinations are less reliable. Finally, at a distance less than two hundred light years the parallax effect of the earth's revolution becomes practically inappreciable. For the great majority of the stars, which are far more remote than this, the direct method fails, at present. Doubtless the limit will be extended somewhat with the construction of larger telescopes. Still more effective would be the plan to secure a wider separation of the two points of observation, now two opposite points of the earth's orbit, if it could be accomplished.

It has been known since the time of William Herschel that our solar system is moving with respect to the surrounding stars in a direction marked roughly by the bright star Vega. Speeding at the rate of twelve miles a second, we traverse in a year a distance twice as great as the diameter of the earth's orbit. As we proceed, the stars seem to pass by in the opposite direction; and this apparent backward displacement is, of course, more conspicuous for the nearer stars. It is a true parallax effect, and one that accumulates as time goes on. If the star is so far away that the effect can not be perceived in a single year, we can wait two years or a longer time until it finally becomes measurable.

At first sight it might seem that the ever-increasing base line described by the movement of the solar system would permit the astronomer to determine eventually the distances of all the stars. It would indeed, if the stars were themselves stationary. But they are all in motion. In practice it is usually impossible to separate the parallactic effect from the peculiar motion of the star. The distances of individual stars can not be measured in this way. The direct attack is still limited to the nearer stars. In recent years, however, other means have been discovered by which the measurements can be extended to enormously greater distances.

The "magnitude" of a star, as we have so far employed the term, is really its apparent magnitude, the conventional measure of its brightness as viewed from the earth. When the apparent magnitude has been found by observation, and if the star's distance is known, it is easily possible to calculate what the magnitude would be at some other specified distance. As the standard distance for this purpose astronomers have adopted ten parsecs, the distance at which the star's heliocentric parallax would be a tenth of a second of arc. The magnitude of the star at this distance is its "absolute magnitude."

The rule for finding the absolute magnitude, M, of any star when its apparent magnitude, m, and distance, d, in parsecs, are known, is: $M = m + 5 - 5 \log d$. Familiarity with logarithms, which the formula requires in practice, will not be needed to understand its significance. Of the three quantities related by this important rule, the apparent magnitude can be ascertained by observation. If now there is some way of learning what the absolute magnitude is, the star's distance can be calculated from the formula. But how can we know the absolute magnitude without previous knowledge of the star's distance? An answer to this question is discovered in the behavior of variable stars.

Thousands of stars are known to be variable in brightness. The reference is not to the twinkling of the stars, but to slower fluctuations, in periods of hours, or days, or even months, or else in unpredictable ways. Many stars vary in light because of eclipses. Apparently single stars, they are in reality very close pairs which are mutually revolving in orbits nearly edgewise, in general, to the earth. As they revolve, these stars undergo mutual eclipses, and at fairly regular intervals, while the eclipses are in progress, the brightness of the pair is reduced. Algol, the winking "Demon Star" in Perseus is a famous example of an eclipsing variable star. Our immediate interest, however, is in another type of stellar variability.

The majority of variable stars are not eclipsing stars. It is generally believed that they are single stars, and that the cause of the fluctuations of their light must reside within the stars themselves. According to the pulsation theory, some and perhaps all intrinsic variable stars are contracting and expanding rhythmically. By contraction they become hotter and brighter; by expansion they are cooled somewhat, and become less luminous. It must be confessed that simple pulsation of this sort does not account satisfactorily for all the phenomena of variable stars. It was proposed originally to explain the typical Cepheid variables.

The star Delta Cephei is representative of this interesting class of variable stars which are known, therefore, as Cepheid variables. Typical stars of this class are yellow like the sun, but they are supergiant stars, much larger and many times brighter intrinsically than the sun. Distinguished in these respects from the ordinary run of stars, they are very rare; probably not more than one star in a million is a typical Cepheid. Yet they are fairly numerous in our skies. High luminosity permits them to be seen beyond the distances at which the lesser stars fade to invisibility. Their light variations are continuous fluctuations to the extent of about one magnitude, in cycles which range from less than a day to several weeks.

Although the cause of the fluctuations of the Cepheids is not yet completely understood, there is little doubt about the remarkable relation which reveals their distances. The length of the period of the light variation increases as the average intrinsic brightness of the star is greater. This period-luminosity relation is clearly shown in Table 3, from recent data by Shapley. The absolute magnitudes are photographic; and they are median magnitudes, that is to say, averages between the magnitudes when the stars are brightest and faintest.

A Cepheid variable star whose fluctuations occur in cycles of a day has the median absolute magnitude -0.3. A little calculation shows that it is therefore 150 times more luminous than the sun. If the period is ten days, the absolute magnitude is −1.9, and the star is five hundred times more luminous than the sun; if the period is a hundred days, the absolute magnitude is −4.6, and the star is actually *six thousand* times brighter than the sun—a supergiant indeed. When these and the other values in Table 3 are plotted, the "period-luminosity curve" which represents the plotted points shows the relation between the period and

TABLE 3

RELATION BETWEEN PERIOD OF LIGHT VARIATION AND ABSOLUTE MAGNITUDE FOR CEPHEID VARIABLE STARS

PERIOD IN DAYS	ABSOLUTE PHOTOGRAPHIC MAGNITUDE
$\frac{1}{2}$	0.0
1	−0.3
5	−1.4
10	−1.9
50	−3.5
100	−4.6

the absolute magnitude. Presumably, this relation holds for any Cepheid variable star anywhere.

Here we have a powerful method of measuring celestial distances. Cepheid variables are widely dispersed in space, and they are such brilliant stars intrinsically, as we have noticed, that they can be seen in remote corners of space. They are visible with the telescope not only in the distant star clouds of the Milky Way, but also in external galaxies. Wherever even a single Cepheid can be observed, it is possible to determine its distance, and therefore the distance of the assemblage of stars with which it is associated. The procedure is simple. Observe the Cepheid until the period of its light variation becomes known. From the period-luminosity curve read the corresponding absolute magnitude, and having in the meantime observed the apparent magnitude, calculate the distance by the rule which has been given.

In addition to the typical Cepheid variables, such as Delta Cephei, whose periods average around a week, there is an almost equally numerous class of variable stars whose periods are not far from half a day. These stars are blue instead of yellow, and not one of them is bright enough to be visible without the telescope. They are especially frequent in some of the great globular star clusters which hover around the outskirts of our Milky Way system. On this account they are known as cluster type Cepheids, or simply as cluster variables.

Cluster variables do not share with typical Cepheids the valuable relation between period and absolute magnitude. But they conform to a rule that is equally remarkable and serviceable for the determination of their distances. Regardless of length of period they have, at least very nearly, the same actual luminosity. Their absolute photographic magnitude is zero, which means that these apparently faint stars are in reality nearly a hundred times more luminous than the sun. The procedure in this case is even simpler than before. In order to be able to calculate the distance of a cluster variable we have only to observe its apparent magnitude.

Cluster variables and typical Cepheids are responsible in large measure for the rapid unfolding of the universe within the past few years. By facilitating the measurements of distances they have made possible such investigations as Shapley's surveys of the system of globular star clusters, Hubble's studies of external galaxies, and the extensive explorations of the Milky Way which are now in progress. These will be described in later chapters. And it will not be forgotten that the new means of evaluating the distance of a star by comparing its absolute and apparent magnitudes requires the knowledge of the transparency of the intervening space. We have first to examine the relations between the absolute magnitudes and the colors of the stars.

It is well known to almost everyone that the bright stars have different colors. The red star Betelgeuse, the blue Rigel diagonally across in the bright quadrilateral of the constellation Orion, and the yellow Capella farther north in the winter sky offer a contrast in color not easily overlooked. The colors of fainter stars are distinguished when their light is concentrated with the telescope, or more easily and accurately by photographic means. Of two stars which seem equally bright to the eye the redder star photographs ordinarily the fainter.

Just as the color of incandescent metal changes from red to blue when its temperature is increased sufficiently, so the color of a star is an indication of its surface temperature. The reddest and therefore the coolest stars have temperatures somewhat less than two thousand degrees on the absolute Centigrade scale, which is about the temperature of melting platinum. Even the coolest stars are very hot. The surfaces of yellow stars like the sun have temperatures around six thousand degrees. Blue stars are still hotter; their temperatures run up as high as twenty or even thirty thousand degrees.

When a star is examined with the spectroscope, its light is seen dispersed into a band of prismatic colors which range from violet to red like the colors of the rainbow. The colored band, or spectrum, is interrupted generally by many dark lines representing the wave lengths on which the star broadcasts its radiation less effectively. Since the first observations of stellar spectra, by Fraunhofer in 1823, it has been known that these lines are not the same for all stars. The pattern of lines increases in complexity with increasing redness of the star.

The photographic study of stellar spectra has been an important part of the work of the Harvard Observatory for nearly half a century. Thousands of photographs of all parts of the sky have been secured with telescopes having large prisms of glass immediately in front of the objectives. The plates show the spectra of the stars instead of the images of the stars themselves. By this means the spectra of more than a quarter of a million stars have been studied and classified.

When the patterns of lines which these spectra contain are arrayed in order of diminishing temperatures of the stars and therefore, in general, in order of increasing redness, it is observed that they grade one into another, forming together an unbroken sequence from the hottest to the coolest stars. Not more than one star in a hundred has a spectrum which does not find a place in the series. As a convenient basis for the descriptions of stellar spectra, six stages along the sequence are denoted successively by the letters B, A, F, G, K, M. These are principal classes in the standard Draper Classification. They are further divided into tenths, so that, for example, a star whose spectrum is halfway between classes BO and AO belongs to class B5.

Stars of spectral class B are blue; lines identified with helium are prominent in their spectra. Many of the bright stars in the constellation Orion are "helium stars." Class A stars, such as Sirius and Vega, are blue also; their spectra are characterized by the great strength of the hydrogen lines. In the spectra of the yellowish class F stars such as Canopus, and of the yellow class G stars, of which the sun and Capella are examples, thousands of lines of the metals become conspicuous. Class K stars, represented by the orange Arcturus, and class M stars, such as the red Betelgeuse, have more complex spectra which are crossed by dark bands as well as lines.

Dark lines in the spectra of the stars are produced, for the most part, by absorption in their atmospheres. Each gaseous element in the atmospheres, helium for example, forms its characteristic pattern. It must be understood that "helium stars" are not more abundantly supplied with this element. So far as we know, all stars contain the same materials, and in about the same proportions. At the high temperatures of the Class B stars helium is especially effective in forming its dark lines. The spectral sequence arises from varying temperature and not from varying chemical composition of the stars.

Our description of stellar spectra is intentionally brief and incomplete. Its purpose is introductory. The point to be emphasized is the relation between the spectral classes and absolute magnitudes of the stars.

As we have already noticed, the stars differ enormously in actual luminosity. Proxima Centauri which is much too faint to be observed with the naked eye is less than half as far away as Sirius which is apparently the brightest star in the heavens. As the distances of many stars became available, it was observed that the absolute magnitudes and spectral classes of the stars are related in a remarkable way. Definitely set forth for the first time by Russell at Princeton, in 1913, the "spectrum-luminosity diagram" has had a profound influence on subsequent astronomical research.

This diagram (Fig. 4) is an array of points, one for each star for which these data are known. The vertical position of the point is determined by the star's absolute magnitude, the horizontal position by its class in the spectral sequence. For the absolutely brightest stars the points are near the top of the diagram; for the reddest stars they lie near the right edge. Together, the points form a sort of reversed figure seven—period (7.), with the diagonal stroke emphasized.

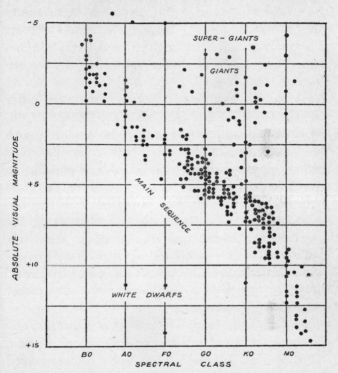

Fig. 4. Spectrum-Luminosity Diagram. (From *Astronomy, An Introduction*, by permission of D. Van Nostrand Company.)

For the majority of the stars, the points are confined within a narrow band which extends from the upper left corner of the diagram to the lower right. This is the "main sequence," and the sun is a member of it. The sun is a yellow star of spectral class GO; its absolute visual magnitude is 4.85, that is to say, at the standard distance of ten parsecs the sun would appear almost as faint as a star of the fifth magnitude.

Along the main sequence the stars become dimmer with increasing redness. At the top are the blue class B stars, some of them ten thousand times more luminous than the sun. We can see them at great distances. At the bottom of the sequence the red class M stars may have only a ten thousandth of the sun's luminosity. The very nearest of these feeble stars can be discerned with the telescope; the more distant ones are invisible. The diminished brightness of these red stars is owing to their lowered temperature, and to their smaller size as well.

How then shall we account for the stars of different colors which are represented by points on the upper branch of our reversed figure seven? They are designated "giants" and "supergiants." Among the latter we find red stars fully fifteen magnitudes—a million times—brighter absolutely than corresponding red stars of the main sequence. But all red stars of the same class, having about the same surface temperature, must be about equally luminous per square foot. Giant stars must accordingly have vastly greater surfaces.

Before astronomers had been able to measure the diameter of any star, there was excellent reason, therefore, for believing that the stars vary enormously in size, and that the red supergiants are the largest of all stars. Accordingly, when Michelson's proposal to measure the diameters of the stars with the interferometer was subjected to experimental test, in 1920, with the great Mount Wilson reflector, it was the red supergiant, Betelgeuse, which was selected.

The measurement showed that Betelgeuse is more than 200 million miles in diameter. It is a supergiant in size as well as in brightness. And the red Antares is nearly twice as large—about 450 times the sun's diameter. The largest star known, Antares contains nevertheless only thirty times more material than our sun, material so widely dispersed that it averages 3000 times rarer than the air around us.

Equally significant are the few points in our diagram which fall far below the main sequence. They represent a remarkable class of white stars which are ten thousand times fainter than the majority of the white stars. These are the "white dwarfs"; among them the faint companion of Sirius is the best known. Comparable in mass with other stars, they resemble the planets in size. They must be thousands of times denser than the earth, or any substance, either natural or artificial, with which we are familiar. Unique among the stars in the surprising degree of their compactness, they stand as a serious threat to any theory of stellar constitution that refuses to include them.

Increasing knowledge of the distances of the celestial bodies has opened fertile fields for astronomical inquiry. As an example, we have touched upon the opportunity which the spectrum-luminosity diagram offers for learning about individual stars. No longer simply twinkling lights to decorate the evening sky, the stars have become in modern minds the building blocks of the vast and complex structure we call the physical universe. They differ surprisingly little in weight; none is less than one fifth the sun's mass, and only a small per cent exceed it more than five times. As we have seen, they differ enormously in size, and therefore in density, and in absolute luminosity.

Still other ways of measuring celestial distances have been discovered in recent years. In no other field of astronomy has the quest been pursued more diligently or with greater reward. Only a century ago, the problem of stellar distances was utterly unsolved; it may well have seemed to many people to be beyond human solution. If it were indeed unsolvable, not merely this Chapter but also those that follow could not have been written.

CHAPTER IV

CLUSTERS OF STARS

THE preference of stars to flock together is as marked as the gregariousness of people, or of birds. We can scarcely call it surprising. It would be surprising indeed, and disappointing as an artistic effort, if nature had chosen to distribute the stars uniformly through space. How the stars were originally gathered into clusters we leave to others, along with the question of how the stars themselves came to be. Our account is of the universe evolving in the mind of man; as it unfolds, we discern more clearly the grouping of the stars in concourses of higher and higher order.

Star clusters are divided by contrasting characteristics into two categories, the open clusters and the globular clusters. The first class is represented by the Pleiades, the second by the great cluster in Hercules.

Open clusters of stars have been designated also as irregular clusters. The term "galactic clusters," which some authorities now definitely prefer, calls attention to their marked concentration around the galactic plane. Although they are associated with the local system of stars around us, the open clusters are not appreciably influenced by the tilt of this system to the principal plane of the star clouds; they crowd toward the Milky Way, and the majority are actually within it. Few indeed of the open clusters are more than 15° from the equatorial circle of the Milky Way. The exceptions are among the nearest clusters.

A star cluster is not a temporary congestion in celestial traffic. Rather, it is a permanent unit proceeding in an orderly way with respect to its surroundings, like a fleet of ships bound on a common errand. Its individual stars are moving with the same speed in the same direction. So far as we know, the only distinction between a binary star, a multiple star, and an open cluster is in extent of membership. The open clusters range in this respect from a few stars to a few thousand. And since they are all in motion, "moving clusters" are those whose motions are conspicuous, often because they are near us.

From the local point of view the Ursa Major cluster is unique. We are within this cluster, although our sun is not a member of it. On this account the individual stars of the cluster are widely dispersed in our skies. The stars of the Great Dipper in the north, with the exception of the end stars, the brightest star of the Northern

Crown, Beta Aurigae, and Sirius in the south are conspicuous among the thirty or more stars which comprise this cluster. Moving all in the same direction, they are leaving us behind; and as they recede along courses which converge apparently, like the rails of a track in the distance, they will eventually assume the appearance of an open cluster.

Next in order of distance is the familiar V-shaped cluster, the Hyades, in Taurus. With the exception of the red Aldebaran, the bright stars of this group, and surrounding stars in an area of the sky fully a dozen times wider than the moon's apparent diameter, about eighty stars altogether, form a typical open cluster. Some 800,000 years ago the cluster passed by the sun at the distance of 65 light years. Now it is twice as far away; and in less than a hundred million years, the Taurus cluster will have shrunk in the distance to a telescopic object not far to the east of Betelgeuse in Orion.

A hundred million years is, of course, a long time. In that interval, if it continues straight ahead at its present speed of nearly thirty miles a second relative to the sun, the Taurus cluster will have attained a distance of 15,000 light years. In the meantime, it has passed through fields of stars, and has perhaps by their influence lost some of its members. But it is estimated that survivors will carry on for a million million years. For all practical purposes the open clusters are permanent features of the celestial scenery.

A line from the star at the end of the handle of the Great Dipper drawn two thirds of the way toward the star Beta in the triangle of Leo directs the eye to the Coma Berenices cluster. Here one might imagine, as Serviss remarks, that the old woman of the nursery rhyme who went to sweep the cobwebs out of the sky had missed one. A field glass shows the separate stars more clearly. While open clusters in general are characterized by their close attachment to the Milky Way, this one is near the north *pole* of the Milky Way. The reason is that it is not very far away. The distance of the Coma cluster is 260 light years.

Three others among the nearest open clusters are well known to watchers of the skies: the Pleiades and Praesepe, about 500 light years distant, and the double cluster in Perseus a little farther away. Seven stars of the Pleiades (Plate 3), or "Seven Sisters," are plainly visible to the naked eye; two or three more are discerned with closer attention, while many others are brought into view by the telescope. Praesepe in Cancer, the "Beehive" cluster, exhibits to the naked eye a feeble glow which a field glass resolves into an assemblage of stars. The double cluster in Perseus, directly in the Milky Way, is revealed with slight optical aid as two associated open clusters.

Trumpler, at the Lick Observatory, has recently published his measurements and estimates of the distances of 334 open clusters, which he considers a fairly complete list of these objects in our stellar system. It was not a simple matter to determine the distances. Almost without exception the open clusters are too remote to give significant parallaxes by the direct method. None of them contains variable stars. In a hundred clusters the spectral classes of a number of stars are known. These and the observed magnitudes of the same stars are the data from which the distances were evaluated.

For any fairly remote cluster we can safely neglect the differences in the distances of the separate stars, because they are such small fractions of the whole distance. For most practical purposes all the stars in the cluster are at the same distance, so that their observed magnitudes have the same relation as their absolute magnitudes. If, therefore, the cluster contains stars of all colors, both main-sequence and giant stars, the diagram showing the relation between their spectral classes and observed magnitudes should have the form of the reversed figure seven. The diagram for the cluster gives the apparent magnitude of any class of stars in the cluster. The standard spectrum luminosity diagram (Fig. 4) gives the absolute magnitude of this class. The comparison of the two reveals the distance, as we have seen. By this procedure Trumpler succeeded in measuring the distances of a hundred open clusters.

When we have observed how large an object appears to be—the angle it fills, and know how far it is away, we can say how large it really is. It is true for clusters whose distances are known. Estimates of their apparent sizes easily become estimates of their actual diameters, in miles or light years. Thus it is found that three fourths of the open clusters have diameters ranging from six to twenty light years. One of the largest of these, containing several hundred stars, occupies no more space than the seventeen stars immediately surrounding the sun.

Open clusters seem to increase in size with increasing distance from the earth. This un-expected result is brought out clearly by the recent investigations we are describing. The diameters of the most distant clusters measured by Trumpler average nearly twice as large as the nearest ones. A progression of this sort is open to suspicion, especially where large numbers of clusters are in-volved, so that individual differences in their

sizes, which certainly exist, are likely to smooth
out in the average, or can be allowed for.

It might be argued that remote open clusters
are really constructed on a larger scale than those
nearer the earth. If this is actually the case, the
reason is unknown. But it is not yet completely
understood, for example, why these clusters
crowd so closely toward the Milky Way, or why
the great globular star clusters are so unneighborly.
Intuitionally, however, we suppose that the more
distant open clusters are not really the larger, and
inquire why they seem to be so.

Practically all determinations of the distances of
celestial objects, except the nearer ones, employ
the simple relation we have already noticed between the three quantities: apparent magnitude,
absolute magnitude, and distance. The first
quantity can be directly observed; the second
must become known independently; the distance
can then be calculated. The relation holds, however, only if the intervening space is perfectly
transparent.

If space is uniformly foggy or dusty, the apparent magnitude of the distant object is made fainter
by absorption of the light during its long journey
to the earth. And the computed distance of the
object is greater than it should be by an amount
which depends on and thus reveals to us the den-

sity of the hazy medium. Accordingly, the size
of the object comes out too large by the same per-
centage. This is precisely the effect that is observed in the open clusters. Its cause may be the
haziness of interstellar space.

In the following chapter we shall find a number
of considerations which suggest that space is not
perfectly transparent. Great dust clouds certainly obscure the view in many directions. At
the same time, it will appear that the cosmic haze
can not be very pronounced in the directions of
the globular clusters and external galaxies. But
these objects are observed outside the Milky Way,
while the open clusters are found mostly within its
confines. Trumpler proposes that we account for
the apparently increasing sizes of these clusters as
the effect of a hazy stratum only a few hundred
light years in thickness lying along the central
plane of the Milky Way.

To produce the observed effect on the diameters
of the clusters the haze must reduce the photographic brightness of a star two thirds of a magnitude for every thousand parsecs of the star's distance, or for every 3250 years that its light travels
through this medium on its way to the earth. In
such a medium, a star at the distance of 3250 light
years appears only half as bright as it would appear
through perfectly transparent space; it seems

therefore to be a third farther away than is really is. At 6500 light years it is measured at nearly twice its real distance, and at 16,000 light years the measured distance is nearly five times greater.

When the observed distances have been corrected for the effect of a hazy medium of this sort, the open clusters so far observed in the galactic system are distributed through a much flattened disk about 3000 light years thick and 30,000 light years in diameter. The cluster system is tilted two or three degrees with respect to the central plane of the Milky Way; and its center lies in the direction of a point in or near the constellation Carina, not far from the direction of the center of our local system of stars.

In its form and size the cluster system resembles the local system, as it has become known through special and general statistical investigations, though its inclination to the whole Milky Way system is not so high. It is reasonable to suppose, at least as far as we have gone, that open clusters are details in the local star cloud, and that they are fairly coextensive with it. Before pursuing this conclusion further, let us examine the more spectacular globular star clusters, and the more extensive system that they form.

Globular clusters differ from open clusters in almost every characteristic we can mention.

Both, of course, are assemblages of stars, and the individual stars are not different from the stars in general. While the open clusters contain tens or hundreds of stars, or in the very richest examples a few thousands, the membership of the separate globular clusters runs into tens and even hundreds of thousands. They are enormous balls of stars— flattened globes, to be sure, a characteristic which informs us that they are rotating globes.

One of nature's devices for compensating gravitation, which by itself might reduce our complex system of stars to a single great lump, is to set the celestial bodies in motion. The centrifugal effect of the rotation of the globular cluster offsets the gravitational urge toward the center, resulting in a stable structure that may well endure as long as its individual stars, unless it is buffeted from without. Perhaps it is this condition which causes the globular clusters to frequent the outskirts of the galactic system, and to avoid the turmoil of the star clouds.

Ninety-three globular clusters are known in our galactic system, and all but a few have been known since the times of the Herschels, although not all were recognized at first as belonging to this category. Doubtless there are others lurking behind the dust clouds which obscure portions of the Milky Way. In addition, ten globular clusters have thus far been detected in the Magellanic Clouds. Probably others are associated with the more distant galaxies also, but it has not yet been possible to see them distinctly.

All but sixteen of the globular clusters rise above the horizon of Chicago, but only sixteen are in the northern celestial hemisphere. Of these the most familiar is Messier 13 in the constellation Hercules. The designation is its running number in the catalogue of 103 bright star clusters and nebulae which Messier, famous as the discoverer of many comets, published in 1781. This cluster is also designated N.G.C. 6205, its number in the more recent and much more extensive *New General Catalogue* prepared by Dreyer.

The "cluster in Hercules" (Plate 3) is among the grandest spectacles which the telescope exhibits visually. Near the zenith in the summer skies of middle northern latitudes, it is an object frequently shown to the visitor at the observatory. It is an imposing ball of suns—fully fifty thousand of them on the photographs with large telescopes; and even more, it is a ball of super-suns. They are supergiants, giants, and the great blue stars of the main sequence. At this distance of 34,000 light years, a star no brighter than our sun would be invisible.

Messier 3 in Canes Venatici, near the Great

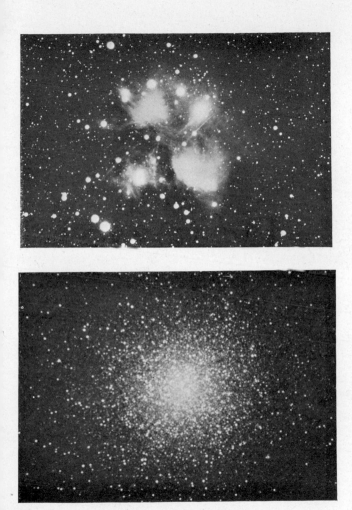

PLATE 3. Star Clusters. (Above) The Pleiades (photographed by Barnard). (Below) Globular Cluster in Hercules (photographed at Dominion Astrophysical Observatory).

Dipper, and Messier 22 in the southern sky, near the "Milk Dipper" in Sagittarius and near the edge of the Milky Way, are other fine examples for observers with telescopes in the northern hemisphere.

In more southern latitudes the splendid clusters Omega Centauri and 47 Tucanae come into view. The latter is only 17° from the south celestial pole; it is in nearly the same direction as the Small Cloud of Magellan, although the Cloud is five times more remote. Brightest of the globular clusters, they are among the nearest, at the distance of 22,000 light years, and among the very few which are visible to the naked eye. They appear as hazy stars of about the fourth magnitude. Through the telescope they are magnificent "chrysanthemums of stars" having apparent diameters nearly as great as that of the full moon.

It is interesting to picture the splendor of the heavens displayed to an observer within a great globular cluster. Fifty thousand super-suns generally within the distance of forty light years, and a still greater throng of average suns would form for him constellations of a complexity and brilliance unknown to us. Stars as bright as Venus at its best would not be unusual. Imagine more than a hundred thousand stars plainly visible at one time to the naked eye. In our skies not more

than two or three thousand can be counted on the
clearest night.

Nearly nine hundred variable stars have been
discovered so far in the globular clusters; and a
third of them are in two clusters, Messier 3 and
Omega Centauri. They are among the nearer
clusters whose stars are more widely separated in
the telescope. It is somewhat surprising, however, that others among the nearer clusters seem to
contain very few variable stars, though the search
for them has been equally thorough. It is certainly surprising that the open clusters, with due
allowance for their smaller memberships, include
not a single variable star of any kind, so far as we
know.

The majority of the variable stars in globular
clusters are cluster type Cepheids; there are typical Cepheids as well. In the account of these two
kinds of variable stars, in Chapter III, we have
emphasized the great service they render in determinations of celestial distances. The former are
believed to have about the same median absolute
magnitude everywhere. Typical Cepheids show a
simple relation between period of the light variation and absolute magnitude, so that the absolute
magnitude of the star becomes known as soon as
the period is known. Appropriate observations in
both cases, therefore, give the distances of these

variable stars, and thus of the clusters which contain them.

Our present knowledge of globular clusters and of the greater system in which they are organized comes in large measure from the work of Shapley, at Mount Wilson and at Harvard. The pioneer in the determination of distances by means of Cepheid variables, he has derived in this way, and in others, the distances of all known globular clusters. In his recently published monograph on *Star Clusters*, Shapley gives the directions, distances, and diameters of the 93 clusters which are associated with our galactic system. From the data it is possible to construct a model of the whole system of these clusters, and to show the sun's location in relation to it.

The distances of the globular clusters range from somewhat less than 20,000 to about 160,000 light years, with the exception of the cluster N.G.C. 7006 whose distance is 185,000 light years. It is the custom, and perhaps a perfectly legitimate one, to emphasize the vast distances of celestial objects by calling specific attention to the long time their light has been on the way. Thus the light by which we see and study the remote N.G.C. 7006 left the cluster before civilized man appeared on the earth. In the meantime, it has been speeding toward the earth at the rate of 186,300 miles a second to bring us the message of fluctuations in the brightness of some of its stars, which occurred 185,000 years ago.

Aside from this and a few other extremely suburban examples, the globular clusters occupy a region of space some 200,000 light years in diameter and about a third as great in thickness. They form a system so symmetrical with respect to the galactic plane that their association with the Milky Way system can scarcely be questioned. Yet none of the globular clusters is found within four degrees of the galactic equator; and Shapley's measurements place not a single one within 4000 light years of its plane. In this central section of our system where almost all its individual stars, open clusters, and nebulae are located there are no globular clusters at all.

With respect to the observed system of the open star clusters our sun occupies a fairly central position, so that we find these clusters in almost every direction along the Milky Way. But the globular clusters are strongly concentrated in one half of the sky, the hemisphere which is centered in the constellation Sagittarius. This fact has been known and commented on by astronomers for a long time. And the significance is evident enough. We are far out of the center.

The center of the system of globular clusters,

according to Shapley, is about 50,000 light years distant in the general direction of the great Sagittarius star cloud. In this direction the center of the galactic system is placed by the statistical work of Seares, as we have noticed. In this direction also, the recent observations of the rotation of the galactic system have located the center of the rotation. These considerations have suggested that the system of globular clusters is concentric with the Milky Way system. They constitute its superstructure, outlining its form and extent while they stand apart from the regions of general stellar congestion.

Open clusters, on the other hand, are closely affiliated with the star clouds. They are assemblages of an entirely different sort in fields already richly strewn with stars. Those that we observe in the galactic system are for the most part details in the local star cloud, according to the interpretation we have been following.

Trumpler presents a different picture in which the open clusters are regarded as coextensive with the entire structure of the Milky Way. The chief difference in distribution, from this point of view, is that they are more strongly concentrated toward the galactic plane than are the stars in general. Brought closer by the correction of their distances for the effect of the hazy stratum along this plane, the open clusters constitute the framework of a system comparable in size with the local cloud of the foregoing theory. It is a lens-shaped galactic structure some 30,000 light years in diameter, differing very little from the statistical "Kapteyn universe," and only one fifth the size of the succeeding spiral system outlined by the globular clusters. It may still have the form of a double armed spiral.

Our account, we must bear in mind, is of the universe unfolding. At any stage a number of different interpretations may be admissible. It does not picture the universe completely unfolded before us. Such a picture would not be wonderful; for we would see in the finished product only a tragic revelation of the arrested development of man's intellect. As long as the mind of man continues to be active, newer and more comprehensive interpretations of natural phenomena will continue to arise, and new mysteries will come forth also to stimulate further inquiry.

Thus far we have given attention to only two kinds of objects in the system, namely, the open star clusters and the globular clusters. Possibly the arrangement of neither special class represents faithfully the distribution in space of the whole system. A model of a city in which only the tall buildings or the golf courses are shown is not likely to give a satisfactory view of the city as a whole. Let us examine the star clouds themselves, and the great dust clouds which hide them in some directions. They are the two most striking features of the Milky Way.

CHAPTER V

STAR CLOUDS AND DUST CLOUDS

THE luminous band around the sky that we call the Milky Way is a most impressive feature of the celestial scenery on a clear moonless night. Pale at best through the haze of the city, it does not compete successfully with the glare of artificial lights. But in the country, on the mountain top, at sea, or wherever the stars sparkle brilliantly against a dark sky, it is a spectacle of remarkable splendor.

Galileo, in 1610, was probably the first to see the Milky Way as "a mass of innumerable stars planted together in clusters." Since its individual stars can not be discerned with the eye alone, the interpretation of this glowing girdle of the sky had remained up to that time a matter for conjecture. A telescope no larger than Galileo's "optick tube" brings out some of the brighter stars. Larger telescopes reveal multitudes of stars assembled in great clouds; but even the largest fails to resolve other great clouds which glow dimly far in the background at a number of places along its course.

Our knowledge of the Milky Way, of its many complexities, its enormous star clouds, and of the dust clouds which obscure it in many directions has been greatly enhanced by the work of E. E. Barnard, for many years astronomer at the Yerkes Observatory. His photographic studies of the Milky Way began as early as 1889, and extended over a third of a century. Fifty of his finest photographs, accompanied by his descriptions of them, appear in *A Photographic Atlas of Selected Regions of the Milky Way*, published in 1927, after his death.

Especially remarkable is that part of the Milky Way that is visible in the late summer and early autumn in the evening skies of middle northern latitudes. At nightfall in September we can trace its course from the northeast horizon through the zenith to the southwest horizon. A single wide stream with occasional side branches which fade away into the sky, it extends upward through Perseus, past its double cluster, through Cassiopeia's Chair, and in Cepheus reaches its northernmost point.

As the broad course of the Milky Way enters the constellation Cygnus from the north—the splendid region of the Northern Cross, nearly overhead during the early evenings of September in the latitude of Chicago, conspicuous dark patches appear within it. A little to the north of Deneb, at the top of the Cross, a dark streak transverse to the stream is frequently mistaken for a cloud. It is in fact a cloud, but not in our atmosphere. It is a cosmic dust cloud, one of the many which hide portions of the Milky Way, the cause of the dark "holes" and "rifts" along its course.

Beginning in Cygnus, the Milky Way is divided into two branches by the great dark rift which continues all the way to the southern horizon, and below it into Centaurus. The entire extent of this rift is nearly a third of the whole circle; and it is not exactly in midstream. The western branch is the broader. It is the brighter branch also, at first, as it passes through Cygnus into Ophiuchus. In the latter constellation it fades and, turning farther west, almost vanishes, becoming brighter again farther south, in Scorpius.

The narrower, eastern branch increases in splendor as it proceeds south through Aquila into the constellation Sagittarius. Here, near the inverted "Milk Dipper," is the most magnificent part of the entire Milky Way. Here, in Barnard's words, "the stars pile up in great cumulus masses like summer clouds."

Here in Sagittarius (Plate 4), we behold a bewildering array of star clouds, dust clouds, star clusters, and nebulae. It is a region of the greatest interest, whether we observe with the unaided

PLATE 4. Region of Sagittarius. This remarkable region of the Milky Way lies in the direction of the center of the galactic system. (Photographed at Mount Wilson Observatory.)

eye or the telescope. It lies in the direction which
has been assigned to the center of the galactic
system; and from this viewpoint some, at least, of
the star clouds of the region belong to the nucleus
of the system.

This region, among the most remarkable in all
the heavens, defies verbal description. It is the
best plan for the reader to observe it himself on a
clear moonless summer evening, to examine Barnard's superb photographs, and to sweep about in
the region with a telescope, if one is available.
Then, if he is part scientist, part poet and philos-
opher, he may catch a glimpse of the significance
of the scene. If he is none of these, he will at least
be fascinated by it, especially when he recalls that
each one of the mighty throng of glimmering
points is a distant sun.

Most impressive of the star clouds in this region
are the Scutum cloud and the great clouds of
Sagittarius. The former, in the little constellation Scutum, is southwest of Aquila. "This,"
Barnard remarks, "the gem of the Milky Way, is
the finest of the star clouds." As a collection,
however, he regarded the great clouds of Sagittarius as "the most magnificent of the galactic
clouds visible from this latitude."

The portion of the Milky Way which we see in
winter is less spectacular. It runs much less to

distinct cloud forms, though it is interrupted in places by obscuring dust clouds. In the early evening in midwinter its course across the sky is from northwest to southeast. Beginning in the constellation Perseus, which is nearly overhead at this season in the latitude of Chicago, we follow the Milky Way through Auriga, and between Gemini and Taurus. This region, where the stream appears faint and thin, is opposite the direction in which the center of the galactic system has been placed. Past the eastern borders of the brilliant Orion and of Canis Major with its bright star Sirius, the luminous stream is traced southward until it disappears below the horizon. South of Canis Major its course through the constellations Puppis and Carina is broad and diffuse, but becomes narrower and brighter as it enters the region of the Southern Cross, the southernmost limit.

Just beyond the Cross (Plate 5) it is interrupted by a dark elliptical "hole" almost as large as the Cross itself, and almost as famous. This is the "coalsack" whose blackness in the midst of the brilliant surroundings impressed the early mariners as it has all who have since observed it. Through Centaurus, at the southern extremity of the long dark rift, and then as a double stream the Milky Way takes its course northward until Scorpius and

PLATE 5. Dark Rifts in the Milky Way. (Above) Dark Rift in Ophiuchus (photographed by Barnard; by courtesy of Yerkes Observatory). (Below) The "Coalsack" near the Southern Cross (photographed at Arequipa station of Harvard Observatory).

Sagittarius are reached again, and the circle is complete.

The "central line" of the Milky Way is a circle encompassing the heavens, whose poles 90 degrees above and below it are the north and south *galactic poles*. The former lies south of the handle of the Great Dipper, in the constellation Coma Berenices, and near the open cluster of stars whose unusual position we have already remarked. Halfway between the poles of the Milky Way, and about a degree north of its central line is the *galactic equator*.

This great circle around the heavens serves in structural astronomy the same purpose that the celestial equator serves in the ordinary positional astronomy. We measure galactic longitude along it, and galactic latitude at right angles to it. The galactic equator is inclined 62 degrees to the celestial equator, crossing it in the constellation Aquila, the point from which celestial longitude is reckoned, and at the opposite point east of Orion.

In the survey of the Milky Way we encounter different kinds of celestial objects and assemblages, particularly those classes which crowd toward its central line. They have been known, therefore, as galactic objects to distingush them from other classes, the extragalactic objects whose distribution is not so ordered. In Chapter VI we examine more carefully the basis for such distinction. At present the attention is directed particularly to the galactic star clouds and to the dark obscuring clouds.

More study will be required before it will be possible to distinguish in all cases between the natural boundaries of star clouds and the obscuring effects of dust clouds. There can scarcely be any question about the distinct character of the Scutum cloud. The Sagittarius cloud, apparently cut up into several divisions, seems well established. Our local system is commonly believed to be another cloud of the same general character.

The dark clouds are often equally convincing. We have mentioned as particularly striking to the naked eye the dark streak above the Northern Cross, the great rift from Cygnus to Centaurus, and the "coalsack" near the Southern Cross. On the photographs of the Milky Way we find dark clouds of various sizes and shapes. As many as 349 are listed and described by Barnard and Miss Calvert. They are very numerous in the general direction of the galactic center, and especially in Ophiuchus where they assume fantastic forms.

"That most of these dark markings which, in a word, ornament this portion of the sky are real dark bodies and not open space can scarcely be questioned." Thus Barnard wrote in his notes some twenty years ago. The dark "rifts" are in general dark obscuring clouds, and not openings in the star clouds through which we look out into the darkness of space. This conclusion, a product of recent years, marks a noteworthy advance in the understanding of the Milky Way.

Dust clouds we have called them. It is believed that they are vast, tenuous masses of finely divided solid material, mixed with gases, and with somewhat larger solid bodies also. The description does not differ greatly from that of the head of a comet. Indeed, it is not improbable that the dark cosmic clouds are closely related to comets, and to meteor swarms as well. The differences that we observe between the phenomena of the dark clouds and of comets may be ascribed, at least in part, to the greater extension of the former. Another point of resemblance is of interest.

As a comet approaches the sun, it becomes brighter; it developes a luminous envelope, the coma, and sometimes an enormous and spectacular tail, spreading out over much greater space than the comet previously occupied, or at any rate seemed to occupy. Similarly, a dark cloud in the neighborhood of a star becomes or developes bright nebulosity. This was set forth as a fairly general rule by the researches of Hubble, in 1922.

Almost every bright nebula has a star or stars,

involved in it or closely associated with it which can be held accountable for its shining. For the diffuse nebulae, the extent of the illuminated region around the star depends on the star's brightness. On photographs which show bright nebulosity around a supergiant star to a distance of 30 light years, the illumination extends only a quarter of a light year from a star no brighter than our sun.

By what means does the star cause the neighboring nebula to be luminous? The light of the nebulosities surrounding Merope and Maia in the Pleiades is the same as that of the involved stars; that is to say, both nebula and star show the same spectrum of dark lines. V. M. Slipher at the Lowell Observatory, after his discovery of this agreement, in 1912, suggested that the nebular light is in such cases simply the reflected starlight.

Yet other bright nebulae show in their spectra patterns of bright lines which do not resemble the spectral patterns of their associated stars. The great nebula in Orion is a well known example. As a general rule, the nebulae in the vicinities of the very hottest stars (hotter than class B1, according to Hubble) shine with a light that is different from that of the stars. Evidently it is not reflected starlight.

It is quite probable that these nebulae are made

luminous by the neighboring stars in the same way that comets are lighted up, and that our upper atmosphere is set glowing with auroral light by something coming from the sun. Whether these effects nearer home are to be ascribed to electrified material radiated by the sun, or to the action of its ultra-violet radiation, or to some other solar agency remains to be definitely established. By further analogy with comets' tails we might venture to suppose not only that these bright nebulae are illuminated by the associated stars, but also that they are produced by their action out of the dark clouds. The relationship between bright and dark nebulae, however, requires further study.

In earlier times all hazy objects in the heavens, except comets and the Milky Way, were known as nebulae. And as more and more of these misty patches were resolved into stars by telescopes of increasing size, it came to be generally believed that nebulae were nothing more than distant clusters of stars. William Herschel had surmised that some nebulae are not of a starry nature, and both Kant and Laplace had pictured the evolution of the solar system out of gaseous nebulae.

It was not until 1864, however, that the existence of gaseous nebulae was definitely established by the spectroscope in the hands of William Huggins. He observed that the light of certain nebulae—the nebulae having bright lines in their spectra—comes not from assemblages of stars, but from glowing gas. Thenceforth, gaseous nebulae and star clusters were sharply set apart.

Gradually the distinction came to be drawn between galactic nebulae, which are concentrated toward the Milky Way, and extragalactic nebulae which do not congregate along its course. The latter, indeed, seem to avoid the Milky Way; but their aversion is only apparent, for it arises reasonably from the obscuring effects of the dark clouds. Finally, in 1925, the so-called extragalactic nebulae, such as the great nebula in Andromeda, were established as vast stellar systems beyond the Milky Way. We now refer to them as external systems, or exterior galaxies.

Thus two classes of celestial objects which were formerly known as nebulae have been separated sharply from the nebulae proper. On the other hand, the dark "rifts" of the Milky Way have proved to be dark nebulae differing from some, at least, of the bright ones only because of the absence of neighboring stars. We find these nebulae, both bright and dark, not only in the galactic system, but in the external systems as well.

The great nebula in Orion is among the brightest and best known of the bright diffuse nebulae in our own system. To the naked eye it appears as the slightly hazy central star of three in Orion's sword. With the telescope it is a remarkable cloudy object, suggesting to Barnard a great ghostly bat, and to Lassell "large masses of cotton-wool packed one behind another, the edges pulled out so as to be very filmy." On the photographs it spreads over a region of the sky more than four times the apparent area of the full moon. At its distance of six hundred light years the diameter of the nebula must, therefore, exceed ten light years.

Equally remarkable on the photographs, though very difficult to discern with the eye at the telescope, are the nebulae around the brighter stars of the Pleiades (Plate 3). The finest surrounds Merope, like a cirrous cloud of intricate structure. They are brighter parts of an enormous nebulosity which covers at least a hundred square degrees of the heavens.

East of Alpha Cygni, at the top of the Northern Cross, the North America nebula is shaped by obscuring clouds in the form of the continent after which it was named by Max Wolf. The photographic studies by this astronomer at Heidelberg have made important contributions to our knowledge of the Milky Way and the objects along its course. Toward the northwest in the same constellation the photographs show a great loop of nebulosity. Its brighter portions are the "network nebula" and "filamentary nebula," whose names describe very well their complex structure, delicate as frostwork.

In northern Scorpius and southern Ophiuchus, which Barnard describes as one of the most extraordinary regions of the sky, an extensive nebula brightens around the conspicuous stars. It is interrupted by dark lanes which extend especially toward the east into the vicinity of Theta Ophiuchi (Plate 5) where the dark clouds take strange shapes. On examining this spectacular array of bright and dark clouds we can readily believe that there is much more to be learned about them. "Sometime," Barnard once remarked, "when we understand them better, all these features may have a different and more important meaning for us."

These are a few of the many diffuse nebulae which lie, for the most part, along or near the course of the Milky Way. A written description is entirely inadequate to present clearly their beauty and their bewildering variety of form and texture. The eye at the telescope discerns them either imperfectly or not at all. It is often left to photographs with long exposures to reveal their filmy light. Excellent collections have been secured at Yerkes, Lick, Mount Wilson, and other observatories. Copies of these photographs are widely distributed, in books and magazines, on lantern slides, and in other ways, so that they are available to almost everyone.

The light of the nebulae is actually very feeble, resembling in this respect the permanent auroral glow in our atmosphere rather than the spectacular streamers and draperies of the aurora. It is faint not because of remoteness, as the light of a distant star might be. For the same angular area the brightness of the nebula remains the same regardless of distance. This is a rule for luminous surfaces. That we can not see the North America nebula in the heavens means that we could not see its light if we were at its center.

In addition to the great diffuse nebulae, we encounter, mostly near the Milky Way, slightly more than a hundred planetary nebulae. These curious objects are so-named because they appear generally as elliptical disks; otherwise they have nothing in common with the planets. None is visible without the telescope. They are flattened globes of nebulous material, flattened evidently because of rotation. Curtis, who has studied the planetary nebulae attentively, comments on the bewildering complexity of their structure, and the almost invariable presence of a central star. This star is held accountable for the light of the nebula, and indeed in all probability for its existence.

The "ring nebula" in Lyra is one of the brightest of the planetaries. A telescope of moderate size shows it clearly as a filmy elliptical ring, though it is really a flattened sphere like the others. The "owl nebula" in Ursa Major contains two dark spots to represent the eyes of the imagined owl's head. The "dumbbell nebula" in Vulpecula derives its name by virtue of the pronounced darkening of the disk near the extremities of its major axis. A fine object of this sort in Aquarius reminds the observer somewhat of the appearance of Saturn and its rings. These are some of the more familiar examples.

Dark dust clouds obscure the stars behind them over as much as a fiftieth of the whole sky. Luminous nebulae spread less opaque veils over other areas. Aside from these, it has been generally supposed that interstellar space is effectively transparent. On this assumption the distances of remote stars have been determined by comparing these apparent and absolute magnitudes, as we saw in Chapter III. If, however, the intervening spaces are not empty, the distances that are measured in this way are all too large, and the resulting picture of the physical universe is drawn on too generous a scale.

Indeed, there are reasons for believing that "empty" space is not perfectly devoid of material.

Some meteors enter the earth's atmosphere with speeds so high that they may well have come from regions beyond the solar system. Quantities of gas and fine dust from the nebulae, like the material in the tails of comets, must be subject to wide dispersion by the repulsive action of associated stars. Shells of gaseous substances are expelled with enormous velocities during the upheavals of the novae, or "new stars." If all the material of the universe had ever been assembled in the stars and nebulae, it is unlikely that it would have remained thus concentrated.

Now a gaseous medium in the interstellar spaces might be expected to absorb from the starlight passing through it selected wave lengths which are characteristic of its chemical constitution. It should cause dark lines to show in the spectra of the stars, in addition to the dark lines which their atmospheres produce. This is precisely what occurs. In accordance with the principle which Doppler and Fizeau explained nearly a century ago, the dark lines in the spectrum of a close double star shift back and forth. They are displaced toward the violet end of the spectrum as the revolving star rushes toward us, and toward the red end as it recedes. Meanwhile, a few dark lines, in particular, two in the violet portion of the spectrum which are absorbed by calcium gas, have not shifted at all.

Moreover, Plaskett at the Dominion Observatory has clearly demonstrated that these same lines in the spectra of single stars are not affected by the motions of the stars toward or away from the earth. And Struve at the Yerkes Observatory has marshalled this data as convincing evidence of a tenuous gaseous medium intervening between these stars and the earth. This medium must be enormously rarer than the best vacuum ever obtained in the laboratory. Yet it can produce the observed absorption on the starlight which must traverse it for many years before reaching our spectroscopes.

If the interstellar gas has the properties of the earth's atmosphere, it should cause a reddening of starlight, like the reddening of the sun when it is near the horizon. The more distant the star, the more pronounced is this effect; the more noticeably the star should shade toward the red from the color ordinarily associated with its class of spectrum.

Technically, the divergence of the star from its natural color is its *color excess*. The values of the color excess that we observe for stars at known distances, if it is surely produced by absorption in the intervening gas, should give information as to its density. What, then, is the evidence? Do the distant stars have the color of the stop light at the cross roads, or is the effect less lurid?

Shapley has found that color excess is practically negligible for the stars in the remote globular clusters.   In the Hercules cluster, and even in the exceptionally distant N.G.C. 7006, whose light requires 180,000 years to reach the earth, the stars have about the same range in color as the stars around us.   And more than this, the colors of the external galaxies—assemblages of stars at distances which are ordinarily expressed in tens of millions of light years—give no evidence of considerable reddening.   At least in the directions of these objects the sunset effect of an intervening medium is not important.   But we must not conclude too hastily that space is therefore almost perfectly transparent.

If the intervening medium is composed of dust rather than gas, it may dim the stars without affecting their color.   Distant stars would then appear fainter than they otherwise should appear, but not any redder.   A few years ago, astronomers might well have feared that a dusty medium would conceal forever all milky ways beyond our own. We are now assured, however, that external galaxies as far away as 250 million light years can be seen with present telescopes.   To this great distance intergalactic space seems to be almost perfectly transparent.   Studies by Shapley and Miss Ames of the supergalaxies in the direction of Coma

Berenices and Virgo have shown that the light we receive from these galaxies is reduced by absorption not more than a two millionth of a magnitude, on the average, for each ten thousand years of its long journey to the earth.

The evidence of the globular clusters is equally convincing. If their light comes to us through an extensive and effective absorbing medium, their distances and therefore their sizes must be measured too large; and the discrepancy would increase with the distance of the cluster. The more remote clusters would seem to be larger than the nearer ones. But this is not the case. Interstellar space in the directions of the globular clusters, at least for the greater part of the way, must be practically transparent. The distances of these clusters are likely to remain as they are now assigned; and the great system which they form, more than 200,000 light years across, as we have noticed, seems to require no serious revision.

There remains the possibility of important absorption effects in a rather thin layer near the central plane of the Milky Way. Loose dust and gas would be likely to assemble in this region of general congestion. Inasmuch as the globular clusters and external galaxies that come under observation are not found near the central line of the Milky Way, their light would traverse this layer for only a small fraction of its journey toward us, and need not be greatly dimmed. The open clusters which are highly concentrated toward the galactic plane would be more noticeably affected by an absorbing layer of this sort.

It was noticed in Chapter IV that from the recent measurements of the distances of open clusters, in which the intervening spaces were supposed at first to be perfectly transparent, the diameters of similar clusters become progressively larger with increasing distance from the earth. This magnification of the more remote clusters is doubtless illusory. It requires explanation. The theory is advanced that absorption of their light makes them seem farther away and therefore larger, and that the absorption takes place in a thin layer extending along the principal plane of the galactic system, like the filling of a sandwich. Complete confirmation of such an absorbing stratum could bring about important modifications of current views concerning the galactic system.

In Chapters IV and V we have examined some of the details which enter into the complex organization of the galactic system: its star clusters, great star clouds, dark dust clouds, and faintly glowing nebulosities. In Chapter VI we consider the system as a whole.

CHAPTER VI

THE SYSTEM OF THE MILKY WAY

THE galactic system, or the system of the Milky Way, is the concourse of stars, bright nebulae, and dark dust clouds around us, whose dominating feature is the Milky Way. Symmetrical arrangement with respect to its central line is the badge of membership by which the various classes of celestial objects within our system are distinguished from the exterior galaxies, in general, millions of light years beyond.

Three different theories of the construction of the galactic system have received the attention of astronomers during the past few years. It is probable that no one of them is entirely correct. It is equally probable that all three contain viewpoints of permanent value, which will be incorporated in another, more nearly complete account in the near future. For the present, it seems unwise either to neglect any one of these theories, or to urge the unreserved acceptance of any particular one. Three different representations of the galactic system are therefore before us for inspection.

The first of the three may be called the classical theory, although it is scarcely more than a dozen years old. It regards the system of globular clusters as the superstructure of the galactic system, which outlines its form and sets an upper limit to the size that can be assigned to it. According to this view the center of the cluster system is the center of the assemblage of star clouds which it encompasses.

As we have seen, the globular clusters are scattered through a thick stratum which is symmetrical with respect to the galactic plane. They occupy a region of space between two and three hundred thousand light years in diameter, depending on the number of stragglers that are included, whose center is 50,000 light years away in the direction of Sagittarius. Since these clusters are more numerous around the center, they are located almost entirely in the hemisphere of the sky in which Sagittarius is central.

Counts of stars, as we have seen also, place the center of the entire galactic system in the same direction and presumably at the same distance; but, as Seares has clearly pointed out, the statistical method does not determine such distances accurately. The local system, some ten thousand light years across, and having its center three hundred light years away in the direction of the constellation Carina, stands out clearly in the statistical results as the particular star cloud to which our sun belongs. Probably it resembles the more distant clouds which together form our Milky Way.

Recent surveys at the Harvard Observatory place the center of the great Sagittarius star clouds at the distance of 50,000 light years, thereby identifying them with the massive nucleus of the galactic system, around which the other star clouds are arranged in a much flattened structure. Analogy with the external galaxies of spiral form, such as the "pinwheel" nebula Messier 33 in the constellation Triangulum (Plate 2), finishes out the picture.

The classical theory, therefore, views the galactic system as a flat spiral organization some 200,000 light years in diameter. From opposite sides of its nucleus formed by the Sagittarius clouds two streams of star clouds emerge and coil around in the same sense. Our local star cloud, in which the sun has a fairly central position, is situated in one of the arms of the spiral, about halfway from the center toward the edge.

From our station near the central plane of the greater system we see the other star clouds in projection as the luminous band around the heavens, which we call the Milky Way, whose brightest part in the direction of Sagittarius includes the star clouds of the central nucleus. The majority of the stars which form our constellations, most of the open star clusters, bright nebulae, and dark dust clouds are members of the local system around us. The globular clusters appear in the outskirts of the galactic system. The external galaxies lie far beyond, themselves milky ways.

Such is the first of three current pictures of the system of the Milky Way which we have to examine. That our sun is a long way from the center of the picture does not impress us unfavorably. The importance of a central position in the galactic system, or of this system again in a higher system of galaxies is not so urgent for us as it might have seemed to the ancient astronomers. Indeed, the location of the center of the physical universe can not now be assigned. It is not even certain that this term has any meaning. Criticism of the classical theory arises from other considerations.

It is by analogy with the external spirals, and not from observation of the galactic system itself that the spiral form is inferred. This statement has somewhat greater significance when we notice, in later pages, that not all external galaxies are spirals. Three or four per cent, of which the Magellanic Clouds are examples, are quite irregular in their construction; the numerous elliptical nebulae also show no evidence of spiral form.

But the outstanding difficulty in viewing our system as a *single* galaxy of any form whatever is owing to the vast size that has been assigned. The diameter of 200,000 light years is five times greater than that of the spiral of Andromeda, among the largest known of the external systems; and it is forty or fifty times greater than the diameter of the average galaxy beyond the Milky Way. We are scarcely willing to believe that our system is the "world's greatest." Our doubt is engendered by considerations of probability, and not by modesty. It exhibits very well the change which has come about in the mind of man concerning his physical status in the universe.

While the static view of the galactic system may well represent its practically unchanging appearance from day to day, we must not lose sight of its dynamic features. It is in fact a mighty moving picture. But to be exhibited as such, the exposures of the film must be separated by thousands of years. One characteristic to be confidently expected in the moving picture of our system is its rotation. The flattening of the system suggests flattening at the poles, and its great extension along the galactic plane may be regarded as the equatorial bulge.

The rotation of the galactic system can scarcely resemble the turning of a wheel whose different parts complete their circuits in the same period. This would be the case only if all parts of the system were joined, or if its material were distributed evenly. But on the theory that the Milky Way system is a single great galaxy, a large part of its mass appears to be concentrated near the center. Thus the rotation of the surrounding portions of the system should resemble more nearly the revolutions of the planets around the sun; the greater the distance from the center, the slower is the motion, and the longer the period of the revolution.

Oort, in Holland in 1927, showed that the observed motions of the stars are as we should expect them to be if the galactic system is rotating in this way (Figure 5). Stars in the direction of the center of the system are passing by the sun; those farther from the center than the sun's distance are falling behind us. Strömberg's discovery, at the Mount Wilson Observatory, that the globular clusters are speeding away from a point in the constellation Cepheus finds a simple explanation as their apparent backward drift owing to the sun's swift revolution in the opposite direction. Lindblad, in Sweden, has raised the interesting question as to whether the wider departure of the globular clusters from the plane of the Milky Way may not be ascribed to the slower rotation and consequently less flattening at the poles of the cluster system.

Interest in the problem has been wide spread. And the available evidence has been generally

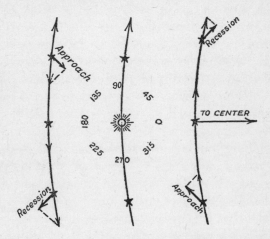

FIG. 5. Rotation of the Galactic System. Observations with the spectroscope show that stars along the Milky Way differing 45° and 225° from the direction of Sagittarius are, on the average, receding from us; stars on the other diagonal are approaching. This would be true if the galactic system is rotating around the Sagittarius cloud at speeds diminishing with increasing distance from the center. (From *Astronomy, An Introduction*, by permission of D. Van Nostrand Company.)

taken to mean that the galactic system is rotating around the center of the Sagittarius cloud. As its share in the rotation the sun is taking us along at the rate of two hundred miles a second in the

direction of Cepheus. Those who adhere to the
theory that the galactic system is a single spiral
structure find further evidence of its rotation by
analogy with the exterior systems. The remote
spirals, such as the "great nebula" in Andromeda
are known to be in rotation.

In the first theory, therefore, we have viewed the
galactic system as a single spiral structure surrounded by a setting of globular clusters. Resembling the external spirals in its assigned form,
in its rotation, and in some other features, it
greatly surpasses even the largest of them in size
and stellar population. If the external systems
are "island universes," then, as Shapley has
remarked, our Milky Way system must be a continent. Later reflection led him, in 1930, to the
proposal that it is instead a group of "islands."

This is the second of the three theories we are
examining. The new construction is accomplished
simply by divesting the classical structure of its
spiral form. By this modification, the assemblage
of star clouds becomes a supergalaxy, or perhaps a
part of one, resembling the groups of external
systems whose description is found in Chapter
VII.

From the new point of view the star clouds of the
galactic system are to be regarded as individual
galaxies, and to be compared with the separate

external systems. If we accept the preliminary measurements, the Sagittarius cloud, around thirty thousand light years in diameter, is somewhat smaller than the Andromeda spiral and the other giant external systems. The local system, whose diameter has been estimated as ten thousand light years, resembles with these dimensions other star clouds of the galactic system, and perhaps the majority of the external systems.

Historically, "galaxy" may not be the most fortunate name for these great building blocks of still greater systems. Originally the word was employed to denote the Milky Way itself, and not the separate assemblages which form it, and which also lie beyond it. A new generic term may eventually come into use. It is not yet the time to formulate a permanent structural nomenclature.

Nor has there been sufficient time since the proposal of the supergalaxy theory to decide definitely whether it will be acceptable as a working theory for the future. The separate star clouds of the galactic system seem now to be comparable in size and luminosity with the external galaxies. In this respect the newer view is the more convincing. On the other hand, the system is collectively much smaller and also more flattened than some of the exterior supergalaxies, as we see in Chapter VII. Both discrepancies disappear, however, if the

Magellanic Clouds and others among the nearest of the galaxies hitherto considered as external are instead members of our own supersystem.

Just as the members of the planetary system received the special attention of the earlier astronomers, so until a very few years ago the members of the local system of stars were the principal objects of sidereal research. Details of the galaxy immediately surrounding us, they occupy the foreground of the celestial scene beyond the solar system. To this galaxy belong the majority of the brighter stars, open clusters, and the more conspicuous bright nebulae and dark dust clouds.

It is by no means certain that the local system has a spiral form. A number of considerations suggest, in fact, that it is an irregular assemblage of lesser groups, resembling the Magellanic Clouds. In such an assemblage it could scarcely be expected that all classes of objects would congregate along the same circle of the sky. While the belt of bright stars is inclined 12° to the galactic equator, the nebulae are concentrated, according to Hubble, both along this equator and in a belt inclined 20° to it; and Trumpler has shown that the open star clusters are crowded toward a circle of the sky whose inclination to the galactic equator is slightly more than two degrees.

But a number of astronomers have not been favorably impressed by the large dimensions assigned to the Milky Way. And the proposal to divide it into separate galaxies does not solve their difficulty. They have preferred, often without convincing evidence to support the preference, to adhere to the original "island universe" theory of Kant, that the external systems are galaxies in the first sense of the word—milky ways like our own. Our system, as they view it, is not a "continent."

This is the third of the three theories to be specially noticed. It assigns to the Milky Way dimensions comparable with those of Herschel's "grindstone" or of the "Kapteyn universe," and occasionally depicts it as a spiral. Nearly ten years ago, before the great spirals were definitely established as external systems, McLaughlin drew a tentative picture of the Milky Way system as a spiral structure not more than forty thousand light years across. It was an amplification of Easton's earlier picture. In this spiral the sun occupies a fairly central position. Far away in the direction of Sagittarius is the center of the much larger system of the globular clusters. This construction reappears in Trumpler's picture of 1930, supported now by newer evidence which he has assembled, and to which we have already referred in Chapter IV.

Trumpler concludes that the majority of the open clusters are arranged in the form of a flat disk whose diameter is about 30,000 light years, and whose thickness is a tenth as great. Two thirds of the clusters are within three hundred light years of the equatorial plane of their system, which is inclined a little more than two degrees to the central plane of the Milky Way. The whole assemblage has the aspect of a great open cluster of clusters.

These clusters are strongly concentrated around the center of their system, which is somewhat more than a thousand light years distant from the sun in the direction of the constellation Vela. Differing only about ten degrees from the direction assigned to the center of the local system, it may be said for the present to be in practical agreement with it. There is no evidence of special concentration of the clusters in the direction of Sagittarius.

Assuming that the Milky Way system is co-extensive, in general, with the system of the open clusters, Trumpler views it as a flat spiral structure having a diameter of thirty thousand light years and a thickness about a fifth as great. Accordingly, our stellar system is less flattened than the system of open clusters, which in turn is less flattened than the hazy stratum, on the existence of which this whole construction depends.

But the larger galactic system of the other theories is more flattened than the assemblage of globular clusters which encloses it. The whole question of the degree of concentration of the various classes of celestial objects toward the Milky Way is of the greatest interest.

In the theory we are examining, the spiral system of the Milky Way is a prominent feature of our super-cluster. It lies near the edge of the throng of globular clusters whose center, as before, is 50,000 light years away in the direction of Sagittarius. Far to the south, the two Magellanic Clouds are other associates. And it is possible, as Lundmark points out, that a "hidden system" of undetermined extent and form may lurk behind the obscuring material of our own system.

Such, in brief, is the present state of our knowledge concerning the structure of the galactic system. It was only six or eight years ago that the system of the Milky Way was first set definitely apart from the external systems. Remarkably rapid progress in the explorations has been made in this short interval, and equally rapid progress may be expected. The succession of dramatic disclosures of the past few years prepares the way for others. That the account is still far from complete adds interest and not disappointment.

To promote the clearest description, we might

have selected one of the current theories of the galactic system and constructed the story around it. Instead, we have presented all three. The reader is left either to choose the view that seems to be the most reasonable, or to reserve final judgment, and as astronomical discoveries of the next few years come forth, to notice which theory seems best to represent the new evidence. In summary, the three theories are:

(1) The system of the Milky Way is a single spiral structure some 200,000 light years in diameter, outlined by the globular clusters. The sun is near the center of one of its star clouds, the local system, about halfway between the massive center and the edge of the great system.

(2) It is a supergalaxy outlined as before by the globular clusters. The local system and other star clouds are separate galaxies comparable with the external galaxies.

(3) It is a single spiral around 30,000 light years in diameter, comparable with the largest external spirals. The sun is not far from its center. It is coextensive with the open clusters, and near the edge of the great system of globular clusters. A hazy stratum only a few hundred light years in thickness extends along its principal plane.

Let us imagine ourselves suddenly transferred from the earth in the direction of the constellation Carina to a point a million light years away. We look around at a black starless sky, perfectly black except in one region where we see a ghostly glow. It is the galactic system. There are other systems in other directions far away in the blackness of the intergalactic spaces, but we can see nothing of them with the naked eye.

The glow we have noticed is elongated; it extends perhaps four times the apparent diameter of the moon, and near it we discern one or more smaller hazy patches. But the view is very indefinite. It is fortunate that a large camera has been brought along. We photograph the glow with a long exposure.

As the exposure proceeds there is ample time to reflect on its significance. Away off there in the distance, near or actually within this glowing area, astronomers on the tiny earth are combining forces to solve one of their outstanding problems. The problem is to obtain a true picture of the vast system of the Milky Way from the observations made within it. What would be its appearance to an outside observer? Our photograph should solve the great problem. Its development would make possible a decisive astronomical discovery.

If one of the three foregoing theories of the Milky Way system is correct, our picture will bear some resemblance to one of the three sketches in

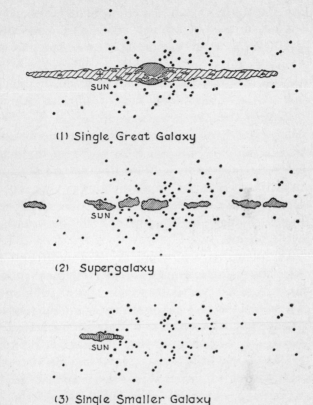

(1) Single Great Galaxy

(2) Supergalaxy

(3) Single Smaller Galaxy

FIG. 6. Three Possible Distant Views of the Galactic System

Figure 6. (1) It will be the picture of a spiral nebula viewed edgewise. The glow that first attracted attention comes then from the nuclear star clouds of Sagittarius. Probably a narrow dark band will be shown stretching nearly centrally across the nucleus, and out across the arms as well. (2) The extent of the system will be the same; but instead of an edgewise spiral we shall see a group of more or less isolated star clouds. In either case the flattened system will be concentric with a much less flattened assemblage of star-like objects on the photograph, which are really the globular clusters. (3) The glowing patch will be delineated as a smaller edgewise spiral bisected by a narrow dark band, and located near the edge of the larger cluster system.

But it is not possible for the present to develop this important photograph. We return to the earth and observe how the astronomers are proceeding systematically from within toward the successful solution of the problem. Their program requires, first, a more thorough exploration of the galactic system, and a more complete understanding of absorption effects within it. Second, further studies are required of the galaxies beyond the Milky Way; these are described in Chapter VII.

Until very recently, the investigations of the structure of the galactic system, apart from analogies with characteristics of the external systems, have depended on counts of stars, or on the observed distributions of the globular and open star clusters. The usual statistical method, however, smooths out the irregularities in which we are specially interested, while any conclusions from the distributions of the clusters are open to the objection that the clusters do not fairly represent the distribution of the star clouds. The present task is the accurate survey of the star clouds themselves, a project whose completion will require from ten to twenty years.

Extensive photographic explorations of the Milky Way are in progress at the Harvard Observatory. Altogether, as many as a hundred thousand photographs will be employed, and it is expected that twenty thousand variable stars in the Milky Way will be discovered and studied. It has been explained how the distance of a Cepheid or a cluster type variable star can be determined. By the detection and observation of many variable stars in the star clouds, it will be possible to establish the distances, dimensions, and forms of the separate clouds, to show how they are related, and finally to combine the conclusions into the picture of the galactic system which we seek.

In the present stage of the inquiry into the nature and extent of the galactic system the Magellanic Clouds occupy a sort of celestial no man's land. Having the appearance of attached portions of the Milky Way, they show, however,

no evidence of connection with it. The Large
Cloud is more than a third of the way and the Small
Cloud is nearly half way in the sky from the central
line of the Milky Way toward its southern pole.
Yet they are nearer the earth than thirty per cent
of the globular clusters which have been assigned
to our system.

Their position in the middleground is of great
strategic importance for the successful outcome of
the present structural investigations. The Clouds
are sufficiently remote to present a comprehensive
view in which the relations of the different features
may be clearly seen. At the same time, they are
near enough to be resolved with the telescope into
separate stars, star clusters, and nebulae. Thus
they form a valuable link between the star clouds
immediately around us, where the relations between details are not so obvious, and the more remote galaxies whose details are not so easily discerned.

The Magellanic Clouds never rise above the
horizon for observers north of the tropical zone.
In more southern latitudes they are plainly visible
to the unaided eye on a clear moonless night as
luminous patches comparable with the brighter
parts of the Milky Way. The Large Cloud
spreads over an area seven degrees in diameter,
having its center 21° from the south celestial pole,

PLATE 6. Large Magellanic Cloud.   (Photographed at Arequipa
station of Harvard Observatory.)

in the constellation Doradus. The Small Cloud is in Tucana; its diameter is about half as great, and its center is 17° from the pole.

Shapley's recent revision of his earlier measurements places the Large Cloud at the distance of 86,000 light years, and assigns to it a diameter of 10,800 light years. The Small Cloud is slightly farther away, at the distance of 95,000 light years; its diameter is 6000 light years. In the space of thirty thousand light years which intervenes between their edges there is nothing to suggest any material connection between the two aggregations. John Herschel's observation to this effect, a century ago, is fully confirmed. The approach to the Small Cloud in particular "is through a desert." It is set "in one of the most barren regions of the heavens."

The Large Magellanic Cloud (Plate 6) is approximately circular. It has the appearance of a faintly luminous and fairly uniform matrix of stars, in which brighter patches are distributed. Brightest of all is the "axis," south of the center; it is a dense cloud of stars five thousand light years in length and about a fifth as wide, with a still more densely populated nucleus. There are other bright regions of coarser texture which contain many open clusters and supergiant stars. According to Miss Mohr's estimates based on careful counts in selected areas there are 214,000 stars in all brighter than zero absolute magnitude. Among them is the variable star S Doradus which is more than a hundred thousand times more luminous than the sun. It is the brightest star on record anywhere, aside from a few "new" stars at the height of their temporary grandeur.

Diffuse nebulae are present in the Large Cloud. And here again a record is established. The nebula 30 Doradus, in a coarse bright patch immediately northeast of the axis, is the largest and brightest of known nebulae of this sort; its diameter is 130 light years. Placed as near us as the great nebula in Orion, it would spread over practically the whole constellation and, as Shapley points out, it would be bright enough to cast strong shadows on the earth's surface. Dark dust clouds are certainly present as well. A hundred open star clusters and eight globular clusters, at least, are recognized in the Large Cloud. The former are themselves clustered, and they do not represent faithfully in their distribution the form and full extent of the entire cloud. The latter may well be in the outskirts of the system.

The two Clouds of Magellan comprise the same kinds of celestial objects that are found in the star clouds of the galactic system proper; they contain stars of the different varieties, star clusters, and nebulae both bright and dark. They are representatives of a common type of celestial structure. If the Magellanic Clouds were in the galactic plane, there would be nothing to distinguish them from the other star clouds of the Milky Way. If they were more remote, they would be undistinguishable from the many irregular exterior galaxies, perhaps several tens of thousands in number within the reach of present telescopes, which are distributed among the great spirals and other external aggregations.

"If the grandeur of a planetary world in which the earth, as a grain of sand, is scarcely perceived, fills the understanding with wonder; with what astonishment are we transported when we behold the infinite multitude of worlds and systems which fill the extension of the Milky Way! But how is this astonishment increased, when we become aware of the fact that all these immense orders of star-worlds again form but one of a number whose termination we do not know, and which perhaps, like the former, is a system inconceivably vast—and yet again but one member in a new combination of numbers."

Thus Kant wrote nearly two centuries ago. At this time, when the universe had scarcely burst through the ancient sphere of the stars, when men were beginning to look past the planetary system into the depths of interstellar space which appalled them, Kant was thinking in terms of galaxies of stars, and galaxies of galaxies. Conjectures they were, but in many respects remarkably fortunate ones, as modern researches have shown. Astronomers are now looking past the system of the Milky Way into the vaster depths of intergalactic space. Let us see what they have found.

CHAPTER VII

BEYOND THE MILKY WAY

IF OUR galactic system with its associated globular clusters and Magellanic Clouds were suddenly erased, the sky would become almost blank. The sun, moon, and planets would vanish, of course. The stars and the Milky Way would entirely disappear. Of all the celestial scenery only two objects would remain, two faintly glowing patches near the place where the square of Pegasus stood—the "great nebula" in Andromeda and Messier 33 in Triangulum. These are the nearest of the external spiral systems, and the only ones visible to the naked eye.

Messier 33 (Plate 2), the fainter of the two, is the nearest of the great spirals. Its distance is 770,000 light years, and its diameter is 15,000 light years. On photographs with large telescopes it appears as a typical "spiral nebula" presented nearly flatwise to us. From opposite sides of the densely populated nucleus two streams of star clouds project and coil in the counterclockwise direction. Dark dust clouds, bright nebulae, and star clusters are included in its organization, in fact so far as can be observed, every kind of celestial object that we find in the system around us.

Whether Messier 33 should be compared with the entire system of the Milky Way or with one of its star clouds remains to be decided by investigations now in progress. Meanwhile, there is no longer any doubt that this and many other spiral structures are external galaxies far beyond the Milky Way. This important conclusion is among the foremost scientific achievements of the past decade.

"Extragalactic nebulae" the great spirals had been called along with other classes of celestial objects which are not concentrated toward the plane of the Milky Way. Indeed, they seem to avoid it. But the avoidance is supposedly only apparent; it is ascribed plausibly enough to obscuration of remote objects in these directions by the absorbing clouds of our own system.

Near the beginning of the present century, Keeler's photographs with the Crossley reflector of the Lick Observatory had drawn attention to the vast numbers of these objects. Gradually there arose a sentiment favorable to the revival of the discarded "island universe" theory of Kant, with the extragalactic nebulae as the islands. But until very recently there was no convincing evidence that they are sufficiently remote.

The recognition of external systems was inaugurated, in 1923, by Shapley's estimate, from observations of its brightest stars, that the aggregation known as N.G.C. 6822 lies beyond the Milky Way. The distance of this fainter replica of the Magellanic Clouds is now given as 625,000 light years, in very fair agreement with the original estimate. Beginning in 1925, Hubble elevated the great spirals to the same high rank. His photographs with the 100-inch reflector permitted the study of separate stars in the arms of the Triangulum and Andromeda spirals. Many of these stars proved to be Cepheid variables; and as we have seen, wherever a Cepheid is found the distance can be measured.

Messier 31, the "great nebula" in Andromeda, is the most famous of the great spirals. It is easily the brightest, though its distance of 800,000 light years is slightly greater than that of Messier 33. It is the most remote object visible to the naked eye. Whoever first noticed its faint glow in the heavens established the record for far-seeing with the eye alone that can never be broken.

Charted long before the invention of the telescope as a hazy spot among the stars, its length equal to the moon's apparent diameter, its width about half as great, the Andromeda nebula remained inscrutable when this instrument was finally directed toward it. Marius, who was perhaps the first, in 1612, to observe it with the telescope, likened its indefinite light to that of a candle shining through horn. Even large telescopes fail to reveal its true character to the eye. On the photographs with these telescopes and with long exposures, the luminous patch is resolved into a spiral structure of remarkable splendor.

Ritchey's photograph of the Andromeda nebula (Plate 7) with the 2-foot reflector of the Yerkes Observatory is among the astronomical masterpieces. The spiral is inclined fifteen degrees from the edgewise position, enough to show clearly the details of its complex construction. Nearly circular in actual outline, it appears in projection as an ellipse spread over an area of the sky across which five full moons could be placed side by side. The real diameter is nearly forty thousand light years. It is a giant among the galaxies.

The "whirlpool nebula," Messier 51 (Plate 8) in Canes Venatici, near the end of the handle of the Great Dipper, is among the grandest of the great spirals. It is presented to us nearly flatwise, which promotes the clear delineation of its convolutions in the photographs; and with large telescopes it has the appearance of a spiral even to the eye. Smaller telescopes show only two hazy spots, the nucleus and a large condensation at the end of one of the arms.

PLATE 7. Great Spiral in Andromeda. Brightest and among the largest of the spirals. (Photographed at Yerkes Observatory.)

The spiral structure of Messier 51 was detected as early as 1845 by the Earl of Rosse, Irish amateur astronomer, with his great reflecting telescope. With him begins the recognition of a few of the "nebulae" as spirals, and the conviction since amply confirmed that there are myriads of the same character—flat double-armed spirals turned at various angles to our line of sight.

Rosse's telescope, six feet in diameter and more than fifty feet long, leviathan of its day, no longer explores the heavens. Neither optically nor mechanically could it meet the exacting requirements for celestial photography. Its huge mirror of polished metal was soon dulled by tarnish. Presently glass replaced metal for the mirrors of reflecting telescopes, serving simply as a foundation of appropriate curvature on which a thin coat of silver is placed and, when it becomes tarnished, easily replaced. The 100-inch reflector on Mount Wilson has silver-on-glass mirrors. The great mirror of the proposed 200-inch reflector will be fashioned from a block of glass, or possibly quartz, nearly *seventeen feet* in diameter and more than two feet thick.

The progress of science in the past century is nowhere more clearly exhibited than in the development of apparatus for the successful exploration of the heavens. Optically the telescope has attained

a remarkable degree of perfection.   Mechanically
it occupies a place of high distinction in this age of
mechanical marvels.   Though its moving parts
weigh more than a hundred tons, the 100-inch
reflector moves with surprising ease and precision.
In the photography of the remote celestial bodies
the separate exposures often extend through many
hours; and during these intervals the photographic
telescopes can be kept directed toward these
bodies with the utmost fidelity, as the clearness of
the modern celestial photograph testifies.

In the many cases where the great spirals are
viewed nearly edgewise (Plate 8), some of their
features are specially emphasized.   The nucleus
has the appearance of a much-flattened globe.
The arms in its equatorial plane are reduced in
projection to a narrow streak on either side.
Most interesting of all, a dark band parallel to
the equator extends across the nucleus and out
along the arms; sometimes it seems to cut the
entire system sharply in two.   Curtis' studies have
shown that the dark band is the rule in the edgewise spirals, and presumably in the great spirals
generally, if we could view them on edge.

In these aspects of the external galaxies we are
reminded of the great rift in our own Milky Way,
the dark band which divides it into two streams
over a third of its course.   Moreover, just as it is

impossible to look into these galaxies in the directions of their equators, so it would seem that we can not look out of our own along the galactic plane to discern the external systems behind the Milky Way. We are reminded also of the narrow absorbing stratum which, as some astronomers suppose, lies along the principal plane of our own system.

Another similarity between the great spirals and our galactic system is found in their rotations. Not only the general flatness of the spirals, but the marked oblateness of the nuclear regions suggests the flattening at the poles of rotating masses. Even more convincing evidence is afforded by the slanting lines in the spectra of the edgewise spirals. Such spectra are difficult to photograph because the light is so faint. It was not until 1914 that Slipher at the Lowell Observatory and Wolf at Heidelberg proved in this way that the spirals are rotating at rates which are expressed in tens and even hundreds of miles a second.

Why the spiral form has been especially appropriate for the building of galaxies is a question we can not answer at present. The majority are constructed after the same general pattern as that of the great spiral in Andromeda whose arms begin to coil as soon as they emerge from the nucleus. Twenty per cent are "barred spirals," in which the convolutions begin at the extemities of a bright, fairly straight bar projecting from opposite sides of the nucleus.

Not all the external galaxies are spirals. Three or four per cent, as has been noted before, are conglomerates resembling the Magellanic Clouds, while many others belong to the third category of "elliptical nebulae." The last named, it should be added, have as yet shown no indication of being resolved into stars.

Elliptical nebulae resemble the nuclei of the spirals, except that the degree of flattening is less. Indeed, some of them appear as nearly circular disks. The flattening of Messier 32, the small companion of the great Andromeda spiral (Plate 7) is twice that of the planet Saturn. The spindle shaped N. G. C. 3115 (Plate 8), an extreme case of flattening, has a polar diameter less than a third the equatorial. Here the equator rises to a sharp edge, suggestive of an intermediate stage between elliptical and spiral systems.

There is an interesting sequence in the forms of all these galaxies, which Hubble and others have taken as the basis for their descriptive classification. At one end of the sequence we have the most nearly globular of the elliptical nebulae. Thence we follow along through forms of increasing ellipticity to the flattest of the spindles, where

PLATE 8. External Galaxies. (Photographed at Mount Wilson Observatory.) (Upper left) Edgewise Spiral in Coma. (Upper right) Elliptical Nebula in Sextans. (Lower left) Supergalaxy in Pegasus. (Lower right) Whirlpool Nebula in Canes Venatici.

It
was
preh
ally
tance
hund
hund
tens
those
milli
hund
of thi
galax
Th
arou
teles
acros
the d
200-i
it sh
milli
as we
thinn
reach
avera
light
Th
of the

the spirals begin; and the sequence separates into two branches, the normal and the barred spirals. At one extremity of the double spiral sequence the nucleus is predominant; the arms are thinly populated and closely coiled. At the other extreme the material is mostly in the arms which are now more open. Here, perhaps we may attach the irregular galaxies such as the Magellanic Clouds, but the continuity is less obvious.

Whether this sequence represents successive stages in a vast scheme of evolution is neither established nor disproved. Jeans has found reasons for attaching such significance to it. Others view the sequence simply as a frame of stable configurations, and find in the present data no indication of the process by which the galaxies attained these configurations. It is an interesting problem.

A century ago, astronomers were looking beyond the solar system to the stars. There was as yet no precise knowledge of their distances, sizes, and constitutions. There was only a very limited understanding of the groupings of the stars, of their motions and the movement of the sun among them. It was not known whether the stars are distributed indefinitely or whether they compose a system of ascertainable extent and form.

These problems are being solved. The stars

out they must eventually; else the whole sky
would blaze with intense light.   What then of the
form and extent of the great system, the metagalaxy, in which they are assembled?   This question confronts us even before the similar one concerning our own Milky Way system is completely
solved.   But let us first notice more carefully the
structural characteristics of that part of the metagalaxy which has so far come under observation.

The celestial bodies are gregarious.   It is a pronounced trait which we have seen all through our
account, and which persists as far as observation
can reach.   Just as there are double stars, multiple
stars, star clusters, and star clouds, so there
are corresponding assemblages of galaxies.   Twin
systems appear in the photographs, not two that
happen to be in the same direction, but double
systems physically related, and sometimes interpenetrating.

Multiple systems appear also—supergalaxies.
The great spiral of Andromeda has two smaller
companions.   Our own Milky Way system is itself
a supergalaxy, in the opinions of some authorities;
and whatever may be the plan of its internal construction, it is certainly accompanied closely by the
Magellanic Clouds.   A supergalaxy in Pegasus
(Plate 8), some 16 million light years away, is a
fine example of a multiple system, and is perhaps

representative, as Shapley points out, of the type of organization of our galactic system. It contains four spirals of the normal type, two of them in contact, and an elliptical nebula whose membership in the group is not so clearly established.

Recent investigations of the external systems have revealed as many as forty supergalaxies. Some of them, as we have seen, have only a few members and may be likened, therefore, to multiple stars. Others contain hundreds of separate galaxies. In population and in form also these "galaxies of galaxies" are analogous to the open star clusters.

Shapley and Miss Ames have made a special study of supersystems in the vicinity of the constellations Coma and Virgo, near the north galactic pole. In an area of the sky ten degrees across they find on the photographs nearly three thousand galaxies. The brighter systems comprise a supergalaxy at the distance of ten million light years; it has a membership of several hundreds and extends beyond this area. Behind this assemblage, three or four times father removed, there is a second group of hundreds of fainter galaxies spread over an area three degrees in diameter. Still farther in the distance, several times more remote than the second throng, the faintest systems to be seen on the photographs congregate in at least two great supergalaxies, each one distributed over a region of the sky four times the apparent area of the full moon.

A supergalaxy of more than usual interest spreads over an area of the sky nearly three degrees across in the southern constellation Centaurus. Preliminary studies at the Harvard Observatory place it at the distance of 150 million light years. The diameter of the group is accordingly around seven million light years. Some of its galaxies are interpenetrating, and some are probably giants comparable in size with the great spiral of Andromeda.

In comparison with such enormous groups of galaxies our own Milky Way system is rather small. Previously we were concerned because it seemed too large. It satisfies us no better to depart from the average by deficit than by excess. But the boundaries of our supergalaxy are not yet definitely surveyed. To the galactic system proper we have already added tentatively the Magellanic Clouds; and we may presently find cause for annexing the Andromeda and Triangulum spirals and other neighboring systems. Natural lines of cleavage will appear with a more complete understanding of the motions of these systems.

The great galaxies and supergalaxies are no

more fixed in position than are their individual stars, or the planets that we may imagine revolving around their stars. Everything in the physical universe, so far as we know, is in motion. It is a manifestation of the fundamental property which we call energy—the ability to produce results, in terms in which we assay celestial bodies and human beings alike.

The spectroscope informs us of the relative motion of a star or other celestial body toward or away from the earth. If the lines in the spectrum are displaced from their normal positions toward the violet, the star is approaching; if they are displaced toward the red, it is receding; and the amount of the displacement reveals the speed of approach or recession, in miles a second. This useful principle applies equally well to the external galaxies. Although the faintness of their light makes it necessary to prolong the separate exposures through the available time of several nights in order to photograph their spectra, yet these photographs are being secured. And the patience and skill that is required to secure them has its reward in a most unexpected and spectacular discovery.

Displacements of the lines in the spectra of the external galaxies are extremely large. This fact by itself might not be considered especially sur-

prising. Great galaxies might well have corre-
spondingly great velocities. But the displacements are almost invariably *toward the red*. They
are almost entirely *velocities of recession*. Further-
more, as the distance of the galaxy is greater, the

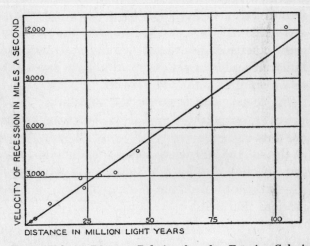

FIG. 7. Velocity-Distance Relation for the Exterior Galaxies.
The velocities, as observed with the spectroscope, increase with increasing distance. Circles represent galaxies, or supergalaxies, so
far measured.   (From a diagram by Humason.)

velocity of recession becomes proportionally
greater. This recent discovery at the Mount
Wilson Observatory has aroused the greatest
interest.

With respect to the galaxies the sun is moving at

a rate somewhat less than two hundred miles a second, a motion which has been interpreted as its share in the rotation of the galactic system. With allowance for this, Hubble and Humason find that the velocity of recession of the external systems increases at the rate of about a hundred miles a second for every million light years increase in distance. As the extreme, thus far, a member of a great cluster of galaxies in Leo at the distance of a hundred million light years exhibits a velocity of recession of *12,000 miles a second*.

Are these velocities to be taken literally? If so, the external galaxies are hastily withdrawing from our part of the universe. Even so, the significance of the rule of increasing speed with increasing distance is not readily understood. It remains for the future to produce an explanation of these motions that will be acceptable to all.

The universe of today resolves itself, therefore, into units of ascending order. The star is the fundamental building block and power house, occurring in different colors and sizes, but containing always something like the same amount of material. Stars are assembled in double and multiple systems, open clusters, globular clusters, star clouds, and galaxies; and in these larger structures clouds of dust and gas have an important place also. Galaxies are grouped in super-galaxies, and these in turn, we may imagine, into a greater system, which may in turn be a unit in a system still more vast. Here, for the present, observation ends and speculation begins.

OTHER TITLES IN A CENTURY OF PROGRESS SERIES

THE STORY OF A BILLION YEARS   (*Geology*)
    WILLIAM O. HOTCHKISS, President Michigan College of Mining
    and Technology, Houghton

CHEMISTRY TRIUMPHANT   (*Industrial Chemistry*)
    WILLIAM J. HALE, Dow Chemical Company, Midland, Michigan

THE QUEEN OF THE SCIENCES   (*Mathematics*)
    E. T. BELL, Department of Mathematics, California Institute
    of Technology, Pasadena

FRONTIERS OF MEDICINE   (*Medicine*)
    MORRIS FISHBEIN, Editor of Journal of American Medical
    Association

THE AMERICAN SECRET   (*Mining and Metallurgical
                             Engineering*)
    THOMAS T. READ, School of Mines, Columbia University, New
    York City

LIFE-GIVING LIGHT   (*Physiological Optics*)
    CHARLES SHEARD, Mayo Foundation, Rochester, Minnesota

ADJUSTMENT AND MASTERY   (*Psychology*)
    ROBERT S. WOODWORTH, Department of Psychology, Columbia
    University, New York City

THE TREATMENT OF STEEL AND PEOPLE   (*Steel
                              Treating*)
    G. M. EATON, Director of Research, Spang, Chalfant & Company,
    Inc., Ambridge, Pennsylvania